The Power of the Double Circle:
A Guide to the Supportive Person Group Process

Philip K. Springer, MD
Shelby E. Havens, ARNP, DNP

ISBN: 978-1-936634-02-6

Library of Congress Number: 2016936921

Double Circle Group
701 SW 80th Drive
Gainesville, Florida 32607

Praise for the Double Circle

"Writing from the heart and guided by personal experiences with patients in a variety of clinical settings, the authors demonstrate their understanding of the structure and function of groups in both psychiatric and non-psychiatric environments. Dr. Springer's experience with patients, as well as years of service as a psychiatric therapist treating prisoners in the Florida Department of Corrections, has enriched his understanding of mental health and well-being. The authors' discussion of the Supportive Person Group Process (SPGP) developed by Dr. Springer and his colleagues while at the University of Florida and detailed in this book are of value to those providing care to those in groups settings. In addition, the authors discuss a wide range of issues of interest to mental health providers, scholars, and researchers."

George J. Warheit
Professor Emeritus
University of Miami
Coral Gables, Florida

"The authors' experiences of medical practice, psychiatry, prison doctoring, prison nursing, AA Twelve Step methodology, and counseling theory all come together in an effort to introduce, promote, and advocate the Supportive Person Group Process (SPGP), also known as the Double Circle, as a bottom-up, lay-driven, self-help for depleted souls technique to the ends of fulfilling and meeting the needs of inclusion, affection, and s e l f - c o n t r o l for those who use this group process. More power to the Double Circle!"

Rev. Gary Hardesty
Ordained and retired pastor with the Presbyterian Church (USA)
Alachua, Florida

"Recovering and healing from the wounds of life's challenges have always been core interests of Phil Springer's personal and professional life. In *The Power of the Double Circle*, Dr. Springer narrates the journey that led him to the development of Supportive Person Group Psychotherapy. I had the great pleasure of bearing witness and participating in the implementation of SPGP while we both were on faculty in the Department of Psychiatry at the University of Florida. One of the significant contributions of the SPGP model is the temporary suspension of hierarchical patterns of participation and communication that promote separateness. When the double circle ceases to be a circle of individual "patients" surrounded by a circle of individual "doctors" and instead seeks to become two circles of vulnerable fellow humans, each daring to engage empathically with one other, first in a dyad and then with other dyads, the possibility increases that everyone might have the profound experience of the existential need to belong. A collection of individuals create a true group. That process in and of itself is therapeutic."

Sandra Arey, PhD
Psychotherapist
Gainesville, Florida

"Dr. Springer has done it again, reaching out in a grassroots effort to help promote, advance, and in many cases regain healthy equilibrium for anyone, but especially for those who serve others and/or puts their very life on the line for their calling in life. His years of expertise as a psychiatrist in private practice, prison psychiatry, and the Florida School for the Deaf and Blind has led him to develop the Supportive Person Group Process known as the Double Circle Group. As a licensed counselor, I have heard lip service to the power of the unspoken and nonverbal communication. The Double Circle Group puts at our fingertips that power known as the 'outer circle'. Once experienced, it becomes clear that we have been yearning for this kind of support all along."

Karen Hardesty, MS Counseling-LMHC
Retired from the Florida Department of Corrections
Starke, Florida

Acknowledgements

We are grateful to those who have made significant contributions to the development of the Double Circle Group by their participation in group sessions. We offer special thanks to Reverend Gary Hardesty, Karen Hardesty, Annie Opuda, John De Paola, Joe Reeves, Tom Hamilton, Bill Witt, Brad Marelia, Emmie Rhoden, Linda Clineman, Richard Besserman, Richard Horton, Michael Springer, Doug Springer, Eric Johnson, Hannah Johnson, Ben Swanson, Ariel Johnson, Marina Johnson, and Susan Springer Johnson. These folks have given many hours of editorial assistance and support to help bring this book to life.

We would also like to thank Patrice Walker and John Shobris for their support and encouragement during this project. We are especially grateful to Bob Baringer, George Warheit, Sandy Arey, and Bill Springer for their consultations about this manuscript, as well as Tyler Kritzer for proofreading and Sharon Julien for the cover design.

Table of Contents

Preface

*"All relationships change the brain - but most important
are the intimate bonds that foster or fail us, altering
the delicate circuits that shape memories, emotions
and that ultimate souvenir, the self."*
-   *Diane Ackerman (American poet)*

*"Your brain sends out vibrations all the time, and your thoughts
affect your life and other people's. They pick up these thoughts and
get changed by them. That's why, say, a pacifist gets caught up in a
riot situation. It's a field of vibrations - you can 'feel' someone else's
thoughts when close to them."*
-   *Bruce Lipton (American biologist)*

Phil's Story

Throughout most of my adult life, I have been in professions that were centered on helping others. Early in my career, I was a family physician with a practice based in southern Mississippi. For ten years I worked with Head Start children as part of my regular medical practice. Head Start is a program that provides comprehensive early childhood education, health, nutrition, and parental involvement services to low-income children and their families. The program's services and resources are designed to foster stable family relationships, enhance children's physical and emotional wellbeing, and establish an environment in which strong cognitive skills can be developed.

In retrospect, I recall how many politically astute people bitterly fought the Head Start program. Subsequently, I believe that programs such as Head Start could have helped to prevent many of the incarcerations of inmates I treated in the Florida state prison system.

In1960, I left my family practice and enrolled in the residency program in the Department of Psychiatry at the University of Florida. Following the completion of my residency requirements, I became an Assistant Professor in the Department of Psychiatry. In this position, I was heavily involved in the training of medical students, psychiatric residents, nurses, and a broad cross-section of other mental health professionals as well. During the last ten years of my professional life, I served as a staff psychiatrist in the state of Florida prison system.

I absorbed a great amount of information and gained extensive valuable experience from service in each of these venues. That knowledge and experience served as the primary objective in writing this book. I am especially interested in describing the development of a group process that my colleagues and I designed for use in stressful human relations environments. It is known as The Supportive Person Group Process (SPGP). My interest in the process can be traced back to my days at the University of Florida.

While performing my training and administrative duties in the Department of Psychiatry, I became very interested in group dynamics and began to develop a program that we identified as Supportive Person Group Process (SPGP). The book you are reading was inspired by a desire to write about what is and has been happening in my life from a personal and professional perspective. I am a recovering alcoholic, a father, a widower, a retired psychiatrist, and former country doctor. When I look for answers to important questions about life's meaning, I am looking for something from the heart. When I say, "written from the heart" it is with humility and compassion, as well as a strong sense of urgency inasmuch as I have reached an 80-year-old mindset. This does not imply any form of frenzy, but rather a firm sense of urgency about what I need to do to make it on this planet for a few more years. As for now, it is with considerable excitement that I bring to light the SPGP as a method of therapy that I had let lie fallow for many years.

Shelby's Story

As long as I can remember, I have been a spiritual seeker. I was strongly influenced by my paternal grandparents back home in Kentucky. My grandmother was my childhood source of inspiration and unconditional love. My grandfather was a Disciples of Christ minister. He and my grandmother studied together at the Lexington Theological Seminary. Although women couldn't be ordained at the time, my grandmother had an important ministry of her own. She held Wednesday night prayer group meetings in the basement of my grandfather's church, and even had her own Christian radio show on a local station at one time.

I saw my grandparents as being vitally important to their small rural community in the Appalachian hills. There were few psychologists, counselors, or social workers in eastern Kentucky in those days. Whenever members of their church became ill or needed money, my grandparents were always available to help provide pastoral counseling, hospital visits, or other support. From my point of view, my grandparents exemplified how a beloved community should be.

When I was growing up, I always knew that I wanted to be in the helping professions. I went to nursing school and also earned a degree in Psychology. I worked as a charge nurse in the crisis stabilization and detox units at a community mental health center, and later as a counselor in a substance abuse treatment program at a women's prison. I led a weekly therapy group at the prison. Sometimes my groups were effective, and my patients were actively engaged in the discussion and seemed to feel better afterwards. But at other times, the conversation fell flat. People shifted in their seats and a few even nodded off to sleep.

I wanted to learn more about group therapy, in order to make a bigger impact and be more effective as group leader. I enrolled in a graduate level program in psychiatric nursing at the University of Florida. I learned a lot about the theories and principles of individual and group psychotherapy. I also became a member of a Unitarian Universalist church, and through this organization I learned how important lay led support groups can be in significantly improving people's lives.

Small group ministries are a vital part of many Unitarian Universalist congregations. In these groups, ten or twelve people meet regularly, usually biweekly or monthly, to reflect on and discuss significant life topics. I found that small groups are great places to get to know other people, and to get to know myself better as well. Over time, participants in these groups often develop deep connections with one another.

In the small groups, conversations are respectful and caring, and can lead to a greater understanding of life. In each session, facilitated by a member, all participants have an opportunity to share their perspectives, tell their stories, and listen deeply. Anyone who is sad, lonely, fearful, or dismayed can feel sustained by fellow group members, regardless of their religious affiliation or beliefs.

Through small group ministry, I heard my commission to care, to build community, and to heal. I believe that groups of ten or twelve people at a time engaging in powerful relationship-building practices can create healthier individuals, families and friendships, and bring communities together to ultimately transform the world. The double circle adds a special dimension to the self-help and support group experience. We are excited about sharing this process with you in this book.

The SPGP

We are now ready to bring this group process forward. This is partly because we recognize that there are stimulating new developments in understanding how the brain works but also because we are being pressured from corporations and government agencies to be more productive without increased compensation. As psychiatry appears to be falling apart before our eyes, a broader and deeper effort to nurture our mental health is finding its way through a bottom-up process in a multitude of self-help groups. With the SPGP, we hope to shed some light on how people communicate their feelings through conversational sharing. It is acknowledged that many people today are feeling overwhelmed and are in search of new methods for dealing with mental health problems. There are several books just out looking at dyadic relationships, or the power of two, as a method for dealing with the problem of being overwhelmed. Dyadic relationships are simply an attempt to work effectively as a pair rather than as a single individual.

The supportive person group process is just that kind of effort. With one person supporting another in a group session, they find that they need to develop techniques for being supportive rather than simply meddling in one another's affairs. What began in the 1970s as an effort to deal with mental health workers and others in a busy psychiatric service has become available to us to use as a learning tool for becoming more effective in dyadic relationships.

There are many ways to explain bottom-up processing, but for the purpose of understanding how the process works in group situations, the evidence is clear that emotions are activated more strongly in bottom-up processing than top-down processing. Lofty and often incomprehensible statements come from top-down processing, such as psychological theories from single theorists, like Freud. But bottom-up processing come from a deeper emotional level and is strongly felt rather than simply thought about and easily discarded. Bottom-up processing is also more democratic than top-down processing. It is like a grassroots effort and in many ways similar to Alcoholics Anonymous.

At present, science is expanding our knowledge about how the brain functions through neuroimaging. We are also becoming more aware of simple techniques in human interaction, which can improve our lives by being involved in quiet conversation or in groups such as AA. We now have the tools to watch the human brain in action through the miracle of functional magnetic imaging (fMRI). Science and technology have made it possible for us to follow emotions and thoughts as they travel through the brain; however, the real test is how we sense what is going on in each other through the magic of just being close and socially intimate. We can get 20 hugs and know how it feels. Now we can also find, through an fMRI, which parts of the brain light up in response to these feelings of appreciation and affection. One of the most startling recent findings is that the aging brain can set up new areas to store memory in the right brain even while the memory area in the left-brain has gone into decay and disuse. Many mysteries lie ahead of us that may someday be solved by the fMRI; however, this brief discussion is not focused on technology, but rather on human interaction at a very elemental level.

It is also important to note that the discussion presented in this chapter is focused on group processes and not necessarily on group psychotherapy only. There is an intelligence in groups that is at first difficult to see, and that can never be seen unless you actually participate in a group. Our thoughts are communicated not simply by words, but we are finding that through the medium of the fMRI these thoughts can be transmitted from person to person without so much as a word being uttered. Others can understand our thoughts without words, just as we can somehow be aware of someone standing silently behind us. With this Supportive Person Group Process, we hope to shed some light on how people communicate with their feelings and body language, as well as with what they say, and perhaps become as astute as some of our dogs.

Anyone who spends a lot of time with a cat or a dog will know that they are capable of reading our moods extremely well, and this is because they are always feeling and reacting to our emotions, as well as observing our behaviors. This is one of the reasons that many people feel so close to their pets. They feel like their cat or dog just "gets" them. There is also a popular notion that a dog is a good judge of character and will not befriend someone he doesn't trust. This is an excellent example of the way animals are easily attuned to people.

During my stint as an assistant professor in the Department of Psychiatry at the University of Florida (1976 - 1983), I had to provide inpatient clinical experiences for the medical students and residents. The question that kept nagging me and the other staff members was how can we educate and/or treat this menagerie of groups we had on our Service. This was a considerable challenge to the staff, because there were so many students and residents, and the patients, who needed to learn as much as possible about psychotherapy. In addition to patients, on any given day our unit often included faculty members, psychiatric residents, nurses, and medical students, and a host of other mental health professionals. Working with this diverse collection of people was indeed challenging. We had to find ways to communicate what we knew about both individual and group therapies.

During my psychiatric residency, one of my colleagues kept urging me to attend the summer sessions of the National Training Labs (NTL) located in Bethel, Maine. I eventually went to the Lab meetings, and the result was a total conviction that group processes and group therapies will be our ultimate pathway to mental and spiritual health. Spiritual health will be discussed in Chapter IX. Many of the ideas presented in this guide have evolved through my experience at the National Training Labs. In 1947, psychologist Kurt Lewin developed the T-group or sensitivity training group. He believed that increased awareness of oneself and others could be accomplished through facilitated group discussions, especially when individual differences are accepted and group members practice appreciation of one another. The development of the Supportive Person Group Process (SPGP) was influenced by the T-groups.

In the 1960s, a considerable amount of psychiatric training was committed to educating future psychiatrists so that they could become psychoanalysts in the tradition of Freud. We are now in a different era that is devoted to promulgating new diagnoses and new medications to combat the assumed new diagnoses. Since the 1960s we have moved abruptly from discovering and nurturing the patient's individual positive personality features to stamping out, in cookie-cutter fashion, a diagnosis based on a checklist and yielding a convenient (to the drug companies) medication treatment.

The word 'supportive' requires some clarification. Generally, the failure in this process is seen as one person meddling in another person's business; however, I found while working with the staff of the Florida School for the Deaf and Blind that a staff member who knew the student well could be very supportive. Being supportive is very delicate process, and the teachers and counselors at the school were amazingly adept at it. But they became supportive through an understanding of the sensitivity of the disabled children, as well as the understanding that the students were willing to be supported if the counselors knew them as they understood themselves.

In this short book, we will bring to your attention both the mystery of the interaction between people at a very fundamental level and a method of exploring human interaction with a simple technique within a particular style of group process. This is done through use of the group configuration by moving the circles inward and outward and also by moving the individual members of the group inward and outward to provide perspective to each participant. The mystery of the double circle happens by the manner in which the flow of energy among participants creates a balance for the group and smoothes the jagged egos of each individual. It is akin to a dance, and can be seen as overcoming the awkwardness that one experiences when learning to dance.

Many people today are feeling overwhelmed. It is obvious that many divorces stem from expectations of each other in the marriage that are simply beyond one's reach. We are also seeing our young people back away from society because they feel overwhelmed. We now look with confidence toward new methods for dealing with these problems.

One of the paradoxes of serving others is that the serving person loses energy and the person being served gains energy. The better the process of serving, the more tired at the end of the day the serving person feels. This is why many people hold back in giving their full attention and energy in the serving role. Intuitively they know what can happen at the end of the day. They feel extraordinarily drained when they have done a good job. This is why we may avoid serving others at times and just go through the motions. This can be a real problem for some people who are trying to do their best to serve others.

One way that one can counteract this problem is to provide methods for energizing those serving. A frequent group process involving the serving ones can be a remarkable rejuvenating force. There are many companies and other organizations that practice this method of rejuvenation using a variety of group methods. In 1947, the T-group was developed for this very purpose. T-group founder Kurt Lewin believed that increased awareness of oneself and others could be accomplished through facilitated group discussions, especially when individual differences are accepted and group members practice appreciation of one another. The Supportive Person Group Process (SPGP) has its roots in the T group model. In this guide, we will be discussing the SPGP in detail.

Before getting too deeply into the issue of supportive person group, it is very important that we at least try to grasp the difference between content of the group and process of the group. Specifically, content would be that the group would contain 12 or 16 members, with their chairs arranged in a circular fashion. The group would be made up of people discussing a particular topic. The process is more difficult to understand. What occurs is essentially an unseen moving and often complex interaction between members. For instance, in baseball there is a very complex interaction process that goes on between the area of second base and first base. The content can be the first baseman, the second baseman, or the shortstop most commonly, but what they go through in order to complete the double play is a process. Some of this can be so rapid that it is difficult to see how it actually happened. When a mother is attempting to make contact with a new infant she is participating in a process that cannot be readily seen; however, it is easy enough to see that there is a mother and a baby in the same place doing something, but we do not always know exactly what they are doing.

We live in a system that is based on economics and extremely short-term thinking and planning. If we were to stop and think for a moment, our world system could be based on raising healthy human beings. We fail over and over again to spend money on the very young as in Head Start programs and jump headlong into spending it on fantastic wars and dreadful prison costs. If one thinks of costs in four-year segments, it remains seemingly intelligent to stick with the economics but if one thinks in terms of the lifespan of a human being then we are clearly on the wrong track. But that is the way of the world. It is sometimes not the one we often desire.

Yet another story leads me to bring up the matter of personality. My wife and I brought seven children into the world with such strikingly diverse personalities that I believe current personality theories must be reviewed in detail. I ask a very simple question concerning personality, but the answer requires a detailed explanation. The question is: Would it not be preferable that we approach mental illness treatment from a strengthening of personality approach rather than from a diagnosis of pathology approach? The personality is part of the human immune system, and as time ravages on within chronic mental illness, the personality is gradually eroded and misshapen. The patient's pathology is not the pivotal issue. The discovery of balance and inner strength within an individual demands our reverent attention. I say reverent because we as humans through centuries of trial and error have gradually developed a soul. We find that this soul development is somehow crucial to the survival of our planet, as we know it. Perhaps the soul is the seat of what we are all about and once we have been damaged, we become tools of the state.

Our high priorities in the Department of Psychiatry at the University of Florida included a desire to provide an inpatient clinical experience to those who functioned on our unit; however, this was challenging because there were so many different professional groups. The ideas presented in this guide have evolved through my experience in National Training Labs (NTL) and, as such, emphasize the enhancement and enrichment of the personality, in contrast to waging war on mental illness.

Dyadic relationships are simply an attempt to work effectively as a pair rather than as a single individual. The supportive person group process is just that kind of effort. With the person supporting another in the group session they find they need to develop techniques for being supportive rather than simply meddling in the partner's affairs. What began in the 1970s as an effort to deal with medical students and a busy psychiatric service has now become available to us to use as a learning tool for becoming more effective in the dyadic relationship.

This book has been in the works for a long period of time. Group therapy has weathered a period of virtually being stamped out by health insurance company regulations and denials; however, the success of Alcoholics Anonymous, which is essentially a form of group therapy, continues to be outstanding. A recent AA meeting in Atlanta drew 60,000 participants. So we have written this book to help those working with a rather complex form of group process to better understand why and how they can proceed. It will be an evolving process and hopefully for the better. Hopefully, on close inspection the users of this group will find that it is helpful in stressful situations that involve co-workers, caregivers, parents, and spouses.

Reference
Lewin, K. (1935). *A dynamic theory of personality*. New York: McGraw Hill.

Introduction

*"Bottom up processing assumes that there
is essential intelligence in our genes that is to be mined and distilled,
and hopefully never ignored."*
- Phil Springer

"Lord, make me an instrument of your peace."
- St. Francis of Assissi

As previously stated in the preface, this book is about an instrument, in that this instrument is a form of group process. Although it is complex, in some ways it is also amazingly simple.

We have been thinking a great deal about what an instrument really is. Is it a knife or a fork, or can it be simply an idea? A gun can be an instrument and can be used for either aggression or defense. An instrument can be many things. In a well-known Christian prayer, St. Francis beseeches God to make him become an instrument of God's peace. So an instrument could be a person. This book is about an instrument that we call the Supportive Person Group Process.

In 1978, when we were just beginning to use this method, I had no idea what the eventual ramifications would be. A bottom-up approach is the piecing together of ideas to give rise to more complex systems, thus turning the original concepts into subsets of the emerging system. Bottom-up processing is a type of information processing based on incoming data from the environment to form a perception.

From a cognitive psychology perspective, information enters the eyes in one direction (sensory input, or the "bottom") and is then turned upside down into an image by our brain that we can recognize and interpret. One might imagine a bottom-up type of phenomenon happening in 1905 as people suffering from tuberculosis gathered for support.

They came into the room one by one, slowly and haltingly, as though at first they did not see each another or at least acknowledge one another's presence. But as providence would have it, a conversation ensued amongst the several tuberculosis patients in Dr. Pratt's waiting room. In 1905 there was no doubt about the ominous nature of tuberculosis; a scourge at the beginning of an otherwise hopeful century, tuberculosis was a killer unmerciful in its pace. This was a waiting room at Massachusetts General Hospital where Dr. Pratt saw his tuberculosis patients one at a time as was customary. Who would have thought that this moment in time was the beginning of group therapy? Dr. Pratt was not a psychologist or a psychiatrist but an internist, so the scene was at least improbable.

Two things happened on that day in 1905 in Dr. Pratt's waiting room. The most important thing was that the people with the problem (reaction to tuberculosis) were unconsciously developing a solution and a new technique while an observer (in this case, Dr. Pratt) saw the results of the conversation among these gravely ill tuberculosis patients and offered to bring them into his office as a group. Thus began group therapy, but only later did it become a part of the fields of psychiatry and psychology.

Happenstance is sometimes the wheelhouse of reality. The origin of group for self-help and healing began much earlier, however. We will explore that phenomenon as a central theme in this guide. There is a mystery in how right-mindedness arises out of a two-person encounter, which we seek to explore in the Supportive Person Group Process or SPGP.

Some years have passed since I first found that Pratt had a personal history. I should say I found that Pratt had a history that I was willing to spend the time and effort to look into. He was certainly not a novice in the psychological arena as I had supposed. He had spent the summers of several years with a close friend and colleague, Joseph Dejerine, who was a neurologist in Paris. They spent vacation time in Switzerland and Pratt learned a great deal from Dejerine during those summers. Am I too presumptive to surmise that Pratt took some of the substance of Dejerine's remarkable efforts into that first meeting with tuberculosis patients? Dejerine believed that human emotion was far more important in healing than thinking. Pratt carried this into his early groups with extraordinary effect. But there would be a fox in the henhouse when Freud came to the United States, and with a few negative remarks he placed a damaging blow to the emerging concept of group therapy. Much of this guide is about the secular versus spiritual debate that has continued to plague psychological healing to this day. As Pratt was establishing community, Freud was basking in his theory of the psychology of the individual. We are now reaping the harvest of an egoist society with hero worship and frequent wars promulgated by leaders who must defend their ego or promote it to win the favor of the people.

My friend and colleague, Meyer Maskin, told me that it is easy to be original if you do not read much. He read a great deal and claimed no originality in his writing. I do not pretend to bring originality in this guide but I do hope to bring some things together that seem to be dangling in the year 2016. What is worth considering is that you may get more help from someone sitting next to you on a bus than from a professional. At least you are assured that it is likely that you are next to a peer on the bus and someone who has some of the same experiences. The professional, on the other hand, may only have faint recollections of a bus ride. This is in part because of the dropping of the shield on the bus, while holding tightly to your secrets in the professional office.

One purpose of this guide is to bring those of us who suffer addiction and mental infirmity closer together with those who have not been bestowed with a mental illness diagnosis. More often than not, people who have not been diagnosed with a mental disorder claim fundamental differences in their own nature compared to those with mental illness. I hesitate because of the gulf of misunderstanding that has brought strife to the mind-body-spirit healers for the 20th century. I do not wish to sully that battlefield; however, should I remain silent, then I would have been cowardly and avoidant. This effort is an attempt to clarify the field in which we live. I suspect that it will take many voices from many clinicians in the healing arts to counter what is happening in psychology and psychiatry today. Psychiatry and psychology have entered a dreadful place in history. They are busy sealing off the semipermeable membrane of our consciousness, which in a more natural world could allow feelings and hesitant thoughts to emerge from the designated patient. Whatever is haltingly uttered is too often received and sullied beyond recognition. I would call this era the one of confrontation, which drives the most tender of egos into the back room, the back porch, and too often into clouds of harmful substances such as alcohol and poorly designed drugs. Those who are the most semipermeable, as the cell membrane is, are the most vulnerable.

After the initial gains made by William James, Joseph Pratt, Carl Jung, and many others, a secular professional group, headed up by Freud, became quite vocal and obvious in the early 1900s. They attempted with considerable success to disenfranchise the spiritual element, which I contend is necessary for human health and healing. The spiritual element could be described as the semipermeable membrane that guards the entrance of every living cell. Many mental health professionals disguise and present themselves under the rubric of professionalism with considerable anti-spiritual bias. They ask for entrance into your thoughts and feelings. But we as frightened individuals frequently close the membrane down and shut out the professional doctor only to turn and open up to the trusted friend. Why not turn the matter over to the expert? Why turn this matter over to the wisdom of the single-cell organism that developed over millions of years on this planet? And how does this simple membrane let some things in and keep other things are out?

To this day, psychiatry is fostered by the pharmaceutical industry, a variety of governmental agencies, and medical and psychological societies. This is a difficult problem to tackle, but many at the grassroots level must accept the challenge. I accept this challenge and I am too old to be shamed into quiet submissiveness. This effort is neither scientific nor unscientific. I believe what my father told me to be true: *Science is a method of discovery, nothing more and nothing less.* Some of the arguments mounted in this guide use the scientific method, but I do not consider them to be science. Through all the years that I knew my father, he never mentioned God but never disparaged religion. I will continue to seek God but have found only indirect evidence of the reality of God. Much of this guide is about such indirect evidence.

Another purpose of this project is to encourage the discovery process and, at the very least, attenuate the territorial process. Joseph Campbell delighted in the discovery of cultures and religions but took neither ownership nor badge of religious preference. Our healing establishment has allowed greed to run the show. I intend to illustrate some of that process and suggest how it can be countered. I also believe that personal responsibility has been foreshadowed by an avaricious legal system, which is heavily participating in killing our spiritual field of play. I propose to offer some targets to the folks who are suffering the politics of commercialism, the religiosity within some churches, the presumptiveness of government, and the impersonal way we are unfortunately treating each other. It is time for a change. It is time for a great healing potential to be unleashed without malice and without the notion of winning.

But how will this happen? As people across the country meet in small groups, whether for knitting, canning vegetables, or deep psychological exchange, they bring spirit with them. They bring their local knowledge, what happened to their child at school and what happened to them at the tax collector's office, and too often what did not happen at the doctor's office. They speak of hours spent in the ER of the local hospital only to find little that is of comfort. The people who meet and share their common plights bring what is needed for this and the next generation. But they are not buying into what is being sold in the secular and medical marketplace.

What we can do is to set the record straight as to how we have come to trust knowledge from the experts too much and trust knowledge and experience from each other too little. We can learn to use our unlimited resources to express heartfelt concerns and receive heartfelt answers. We hope to show that in the small group, imagery is laid bare and idolatry is thrown out the side door. But seeking the nurturance and the opportunity to compassionately share our experiences within the small group is worth the price of regular attendance. We can trust each other's experience more readily than we can trust the theory of an expert because we have knowledge of each other's experience.

I have put off until the last paragraph with humble hesitancy a bomb rolling into the center of the "field of play". This is the notion that I have carried for at least 30 years: *Successful therapy emerges as a change in the personality rather than in the correction of an element of a defined illness such as schizophrenia, major depression, or the newly-hatched attention deficit hyperactive disorder (ADHD).* This is not a new idea but an ancient one. The concept of personality change was introduced by the apostle Paul more than 2000 years ago in the New Testament in Romans 5:3 with the following: "And not only so, but we glory in tribulations also; knowing that tribulation worketh patience; and patience, experience; and experience, hope".

My recollection of the therapeutic miracles I have witnessed is in the process of the agony of tribulation followed by agony of patience and of prolonged experience, which inevitably leads to hope. This change in personality arrives as the appointed patients begin to work from within their souls. Centuries later, Viktor Frankl would write in a very similar vein in his guide *Man's Search for Meaning*: "Thus suffering completely fills the human soul and conscious mind, no matter whether the suffering is great or little. Therefore the 'size' of human suffering   is   absolutely   relative".

I will attempt to bring the Alcoholics Anonymous message as a continuing baton, sharing about the struggle between our divided selves and between each other. It is a constantly evolving process; however, much of the success of Alcoholics Anonymous could be attributed to its steadfast application of the Twelve Steps in the original form over at least eight decades.

I wish to begin this guide with an apology for my failing to have dug deeply enough into the body of literature concerning group therapy to come forth with any truly new ideas; however, this work is not only intended for a regular audience of readers but also a series of notes to my former patients, students, colleagues, family and friends and enemies (by chance alone). Many conversations have been broken off when I chased after another windmill without completing conversations with many of you.

The target audience for this book also includes those who find themselves in a trap made by the pressure of supervisors and corporate moguls and by politicians who have been elevated in the scheme of things to a position where they no longer see the big picture but claim to know the big picture nevertheless.

The advent of self-publishing offers all a chance at writing a guide that will find its way into someone's lap. I hope to draw you in with a warm tone and a sharing presumption. God may know how desperately I have wanted to do this. There have been many times that I have held back and not said something that I knew at the time should have been uttered.

In Chapter I, we will undertake the task of what group process is about and how group therapy has evolved. I hope to guide you along a path of evolutionary psychology demonstrating the development of the family and tribal relationships into the 21st century morass of countless individuals seeking home.

"If small groups are included in the decision-making process, then they should be allowed to make decisions. If an organization sets up teams and then uses them for purely advisory purposes, it loses the true advantage that a team has: namely, collective wisdom."
— James Surowiecki

In Chapter II, we will discuss how psychiatry and psychology have failed us. I will give a picture of confusion in psychiatry in particular through its attempt to accommodate to the insurance industry so as to achieve higher income.

"Never be afraid to raise your voice for honesty and truth and compassion against injustice and lying and greed. If people all over the world...would do this, it would change the earth."
— William Faulkner

In Chapter III, we will bring forth the issue of personality as we awkwardly conceive of it in our current psychology and psychiatry literature, and we will recommend some fresh looks at personality. Is it just something in your high school yearbook or something much more? In this chapter, we will discuss personality as the eventual moderator of our life path.

"The meeting of two personalities is like the contact of two chemical substances: if there is any reaction, both are transformed."
— Carl Jung

In Chapter IV, we will discuss how Alcoholics Anonymous has become a worldwide stable institution and present some suggestions on why this has come about. Again, the issue of personality will be raised and how the principles of AA have a bearing on the long-term results because of the changes in personality seen in members of AA.

In Chapter V, we will discuss some of the features of AA sponsorship and the similarity to the supportive person (dyad) relationship.

"The world is not comprehensible, but it is embraceable: through the embracing of one of its beings" - Martin Buber

In Chapter VI, we will explore the basis for the double circle and how it functions. A variety of issues are discussed, including the relationship within the supportive person dyad and its effect on the ego function of each individual in the dyad.

"The individuals in great dyads will be very different from each other and very much alike. These simultaneous extremes generate the deep rapport and energizing friction that define a creative pair."
— Joshua Wolf Shenk

Chapter VII explores the rationale for support groups, with or without a problem focus such as alcoholism or drug addiction. In the words of the comic strip character Pogo, *"We have met the enemy and it is us!"* But on a more serious level, we are faced with alienation from each other via historical acceleration via rampant commercialism.

Chapter VIII presents the notion that through an understanding of our evolutionary past we can find ways to evolve without so much guilt over character defects and the compulsion to throw ourselves away because of presumed worthlessness.

"It is not the strongest or the most intelligent who will survive but those who can best manage change." — Charles Darwin

Chapter IX is an attempt to shed light on the raging conflict between secular and spiritual roots in psychology and psychiatry. This polarization is not necessarily a bad thing, but is a part of our world of debate about major issues throughout the history of civilization. We have seen many religions come and go as well as forms of psychology that have not stood the test of time. Although the secularization of psychology and psychiatry has been considered useful for clarity of purpose and scientific rigor, many clinicians (such as the authors of this text) consider spiritual issues vital to the therapeutic process. There has been a recent resurgence of cognitive behavioral therapy within psychology; however, there has been a continuing spiritual focus within self-help groups. Had it not been for Alcoholics Anonymous and other twelve-step groups, spiritual treatments might have been snuffed out.

In Chapter X we outline the group configuration that is unique in Supportive Person Group Process. SPGP seeks to help the participants overcome shyness and underdeveloped ego as well as attenuate the effect of those whose ego is so strong that it is taking over the group. The SPGP has features that are at first difficult to see but ultimately serve to bring group process to a higher level than conventional group. This is accomplished through positioning or configuration. In Chapter X we also develop the idea that a pair of participants can bring each of the individuals in the pair to a greater strength of interaction as well as discovering the altruism of being supportive of another person.

Chapter XI discusses the potential benefits of using the SPGP with special populations such as people who work in high-stress occupations. We also discuss the possibility of future research that will validate the benefits and outcomes of the Double Circle SPGP model.

Last but not least, Chapter XII will provide a conclusion and recap of the rationale for the Double Circle group process and how it can be used in a wide variety of settings. We will briefly summarize the benefits of this model and our vision for transforming groups and communities through the use of this very special process.

References

Buber, M. (1947). *Between man and man.* New York: Routledge Publications.

Campbell, J. & Moyers, B. (1991). *The power of myth.* New York: Anchor Books.

Darwin, C. (2003). *The origin of species: 150th anniversary edition.* New York: Signet Classics.

Dejerine, J. & Gauckler, E. (1923). *The psychoneuroses and their treatment by psychotherapy.* Charleston, SC: Nabu Press.

Faulkner, W. (1954). *The Faulkner reader: Selections from the works of William Faulkner.* New York: Random House.

Frankl, V. (1959). *Man's search for meaning.* New York: Washington Square Press.

Freud, S. (2013). *A general introduction to psychoanalysis (classic reprint).* London: Forgotten Books.

James, W. (1950). *Principles of psychology.* Mineola, NY: Dover Publications.

Jung, C. (1960). *Psychology and religion.* New Haven, CT: Yale University Press.

Maskin, M. (1989). *Wisdom and wit: A collection of papers.* Portsmouth, NH: P. E. Randall Publisher.

Shenk, J. (2014). *Powers of two: Finding the essence of innovation in creative pairs.* Boston: Houghton Mifflin Harcourt.

Surowiecki, J. (2005). *The wisdom of crowds.* New York: Anchor Books.

Chapter I

What is Group Process?

"What if humans are in conversation the way fish are in water?"
– Juanita Brown
(co-founder of the World Café conversational process)

"As you navigate through the rest of your life, be open to
collaboration. Other people and other people's ideas are often better
than your own. Find a group of people who challenge and inspire
you, spend a lot of time with them, and it will change your life." –
Amy Poehler (American writer and actress)

If group is anything at all it is a dynamic process. This means that one's attention is focused on the interaction *between people* rather than trying to focus on the individuals within the group. Although an individual member of a group may make a statement that is profound or even embarrassing, the issue in group process is what the impact of such a statement is on the group. Some years ago, Schutz described the process as beginning with an attempt to reach inclusion, which meant that the various members recognize that they are there for similar reasons, allowing them to feel a sense of connectedness to each other. From thence the group establishes rules and controls that offer cohesion, order, and a sense of a common ground. While these controls are being established, a sense of awareness of growing affection that the members have for each other develops, which allows them to be open, honest, allowing and caring. This three-stage process is considered by many as the essential feature of group therapy as opposed to individual therapy. The net effect of this is the group's ability to work at a level deeper than ego defenses and ego aggressive behaviors. In contrast, therapists working with individuals during Schutz's era were essentially attempting to reach below the ego with questionably effective techniques such as free association.

Group Psychotherapy

Group psychotherapy is a type of treatment that involves one or more mental health professionals working with several people at the same time. This type of therapy is practiced in a variety of settings, such as clinics, hospitals, and community mental health centers. Patients who share common concerns or problems are often placed in therapy groups where they can share their mutual struggles and feelings. Individuals are typically referred for group therapy by a mental health professional such as a psychiatrist or psychologist.

Group therapy is often used in conjunction with other treatments like as psychotropic medication and individual counseling. Group psychotherapy can be useful in the treatment of mental disorders such as depression and post-traumatic stress disorder. According to Yalom, participants in group therapy commonly derive benefits such as gaining a sense of acceptance and belonging, and sharing experiences with others that results in relief from stress, guilt, and emotional pain. Group therapy can also help people improve their social, interpersonal, and coping skills. Patients who have serious disorders such as psychosis, suicidal feelings, or brain injuries may not be appropriate for group therapy.

Therapy groups can be as small as three or four people, but generally involve between seven and twelve participants. Group membership may be open or closed. A session might begin with people introducing themselves and sharing the reason they came to the group. The manner in which the group is conducted depends upon the purpose and goals of the group. Some therapists might encourage a free-form style of dialogue, whereas others might have a specific plan for each session. Groups may meet indefinitely, or for a predetermined number of weeks or months. The group might meet once or twice weekly, or at some other interval. In the group meetings, chairs are typically placed in a circle so that participants can see one another. The sessions generally last about an hour.

Group psychotherapy allows people to receive encouragement from others in the group, as well as serve as role models for fellow members. It provides a setting in which participants can practice new behaviors and express feelings in a setting that is emotionally safe. Some groups have rules restricting social contact among members outside of the group.

Patients typically enter therapy hoping to decrease their suffering and improve their lives. Yalom wrote that because every member in a therapy group is inevitably at a different point on the coping continuum and experiences personal growth at a different rate, watching other members cope with and overcome similar problems successfully instills hope and inspiration. New members or those who are in despair may be particularly encouraged by others' positive changes and insights.

One common feeling among group psychotherapy members, especially in the early stages of the group, is that of being isolated, unique, and separate from others. Many people who enter group therapy have difficulty maintaining interpersonal relationships and may feel unlikable or unlovable. Therapy groups can provide a powerful antidote to such feelings. For some members, it could be the first time they feel understood and similar to others. According to Yalom, enormous relief often accompanies the recognition that they are not alone. This is a special benefit of group therapy.

Therapy groups also give participants an opportunity to help other people. Patients with psychiatric problems often believe they have little to offer others because they have needed so much help themselves, thus leading to feelings of inadequacy. The process of altruism is a powerful therapeutic tool that can greatly enhance participants' self-esteem and feelings of self-worth.

Group therapy in the United States can be traced back more than one hundred years. In 1905, a Boston physician named Joseph Pratt formed groups of impoverished patients suffering from a common illness - tuberculosis. Pratt believed that these patients could provide one another mutual assistance and support.

Self-Help Groups

Self-help groups, as opposed to therapy groups, provide mutual support among peers. Self-help groups are not considered treatments for psychiatric disorders. These groups fall outside the realm of psychotherapy. Although they are not led by professional psychotherapists, these groups can offer many of the same benefits, including social support, the opportunity to identify with others, and the sense of belonging that makes group therapy widely effective.

Self-help groups generally have a specific purpose for satisfying a common need, coping with a life-disrupting problem, or overcoming shared handicaps. Peer support is social, educational, or emotional in nature and is mutually provided by lay persons with similar conditions. There is some type of mutual agreement on what is considered helpful or within the scope of the group. Self-help groups are less bureaucratic than therapy groups and tend to operate on more of a grassroots level.

According to Wollert, the group can become like a miniature society that functions as a buffer between the members and the rest of the world. The most essential processes are those that meet personal and social needs within an environment of safety, simplicity, and support. Complex psychological theories, systematic behavior change techniques, and detailed cognitive methods are not appropriate for self-help groups. No two self-help groups are exactly alike. The composition and attitudes of the group are influenced by the group's identity and environment. Examples of self-help groups include cancer patient support groups, single parenting groups, and Alcoholics Anonymous.

The Oxford Group

The Oxford Group was a Christian evangelical movement founded by Protestant minister Frank Buchman in the 1920s. Buchman believed that the root of all personal problems resulted from selfishness and fear. The answer, according to Buchman, was to surrender one's life to God's plan. The group, which emphasized self-survey, confession, and service, was quite popular by the 1930s. It would gradually morph into Alcoholics Anonymous, as membership in Alcoholics Anonymous preferred a less evangelical posture and a less stringent demand on belief in God. The group process in Alcoholics Anonymous is quite different than the Oxford Group, but it appears, in many instances to have a similar effect on the participants' sense of enlightenment and progress.

Psychodrama and Gestalt Therapy

Although Yalom is credited with much of the development of modern group psychotherapy, psychodrama and Gestalt therapy (which utilizes certain techniques taken from psychodrama) had a significant impact on what we know of today as group therapy.

In psychodrama, which was developed by psychiatrist Jacob Moreno, participants use role playing, impromptu dramatization, and self-presentation within a group scenario, in order to gain insight into their lives. Group members function as therapeutic agents for each other's scenes. Psychodrama brings conflicts into the present, using dramatic action as a way of helping group members solve their problems. Catharsis, which is the therapeutic release of emotions followed by a feeling of relief, plays an important role in this type of group. Psychodrama can be especially helpful for people who find it difficult to express their feelings in words.

Psychodrama may be used in a variety of clinical and community-based settings, and is most often utilized in a group scenario, in which each person in the group can become a therapeutic agent for each other's scenes. It is technically not a form of group therapy. It is instead an individual psychotherapy that is carried out within a group setting. Psychodrama is best conducted and produced by a person trained in the method, called a psychodrama director.

Gestalt therapy, which was developed by Fritz Perls and his colleagues, focuses on a person's experience in the present moment, process over content (what is actually happening as opposed to what is being talked about), and the environmental and social contexts of a person's life or learning to understand oneself in relationship to others.

Moreno was an early pioneer of group work. He promoted many variations of this general approach, including working with couples or families conjointly, throughout his career. Moreno foresaw many of the benefits of group therapy at a time when clinical practice was focusing almost entirely on the individual approach.

Encounter Groups

When T-groups, also known as sensitivity training groups or training groups, began around 1947 they were followed by a virtual explosion of group process in a variety of ways. The most maligned was the EST (Erhard Seminar Training) encounter group. According to a Wikipedia account, over the course of nine days, participants were cajoled, shouted at, and emotionally battered, until they agreed they had finally "got it" - a state akin to a religious conversion. Participants were instructed not to wear watches, not to talk unless permitted by the trainer, not to leave their seats, not to eat, and not to go to the bathroom except during breaks separated by many hours. The net effect, however, left many with their fragile personalities in shambles. There may have been considerable ego damage in these groups, although some participants reported very positive "transformations". But on the whole, the original T-Groups fostered a succession of styles that greatly enhanced the cause of psychological awareness and group cooperation.

The Supportive Person Group Process (SPGP)

With the goals of psychological awareness and group cooperation in mind, we have designed the Supportive Person Process as a group, which focuses on the dyad rather than the individual. There is the implied strength of two individuals placing their personalities into the mix of the group as a pair of souls who have agreed to act as one. In the beginning each patient in our SPGP sessions had a staff member, medical student, psychiatry resident, or nurse sitting behind and to the right shoulder so as to be able to see and hear the inner circle. In some cases the patients were unknown by the designated supportive person but they soon got to know them or otherwise their role as supportive person would be fruitless. We began using this process in 1978.

Should you ever find yourself in the inner circle of a SPGP session you'll experience an intensity that is totally different from a single circle group. It was necessary to recognize this intensity and realize that it had to be moderated and controlled or otherwise the group would sit in embarrassed and anxious silence.

Our session would begin with a quiet visit between the inner circle patient and their respective supportive person; this could go on for up to ten minutes. It was often difficult to break off into the beginning of the formal group process because it's much more comfortable to talk in a one-to-one relationship than it is to talk in a group. This perspective is most important and the shifting of that perspective from one-to-one and back to the group is crucial to the uniqueness of SPGP. I would start by telling everyone that we would return to the one-to-one situation periodically to bring fresh material from that process and breathe easily for a while. Sometimes it was necessary to provide a subject to discuss, but often it was not necessary and the patients generally were positive about having a supportive person. I would then discuss some of the rules that the support person would have to follow. While the session was in progress, the supportive person was not allowed to speak without permission from their counterpart or an understanding that they had some tacit permission to speak on behalf of their counterpart. The patients were advised that they could deny what the supportive person was saying as either true or not true or helpful. A great deal had to be worked out between the supportive person and their patient in these one-to-one periods. It was also helpful to know something about the patient before the support person entered the room. But generally speaking, the discussion within the inner circle proceeded with the group leader moderating that discussion and pointing out similarities and using the methods that were customary for group therapy as outlined by Yalom.

Metaphorically speaking, one can see the inner circle as the engine and the outer circle as a supercharger of the engine. The supercharger is not totally necessary except to move the group in a more intense manner than one would see in a regular group. The outer circle provides intensity and coaches the group toward more self-assertion and self-disclosure.

The next step in the SPGP was to simply reverse the circles so that the staff was in the inner circle and the patients were in the outer circle available for support so to speak, or just listening to what the inner circle had to talk about. The inner circle generally talked about coming to understand what their patients were about and how to be supportive, but they were very aware of how easy it was to meddle in the process rather than being supportive. Once in the inner circle the staff also felt the same intensity that they only observed in the previous configuration. It was customary for me to then return them to the original configuration and resume the one-to-one session so as to reflect on their impressions of what had happened. Over time, we encouraged the staff to not only get to know their counterparts better but also to help them present problems in group that the patients felt were too personal to voice. The supportive person was usually able to help them find a way to present the problem or issue with both clarity and ease. It was also a time for the patients to see what they wanted and expected in a supporting person. The support person could share his or her own personal experiences with them as well.

What I set out to do was to keep the medical students from talking to the patients as if they were police detectives to a new concept in group psychotherapy. I personally became much more aware of the importance of empathic support of the patient's life in contrast to examination of the patient's life. Soon thereafter, the medical students were able to visit with their patients in a private one-to-one situation and then be helpful in the patients' quests to be able to interact in group. The intensity was profound especially within the inner circle. I found it necessary to break the group interaction periodically to visit with each one's supportive person simply because the tension was so high. But this became a very helpful breathing exercise in which we found that the group does have a respiratory or breathing process.

The most troublesome feature of the first groups in1978 was that the people in the outer circle frequently blurted out something they thought was important but then realized that they were not supposed to speak in that context. The outer circle was definitely a place of safety, at least the safety to make comments even when not appropriate to the moment. We soon began working on how to allow the supportive person in the outer circle to make comments. We elected to allow the person in the inner circle to accept comments from his alter ego or supportive person in the outer circle. We called this "talking through". At times the person in the inner circle would say that the comments were inappropriate and did not fit with what they were thinking. I would then generally have the group rejoin the one-to-one interactions so as to clarify these issues.

What we were not able to do with this group initially was to help the patients find a way to express feelings through the consultation with a supportive person. We had really thought about it at the time but the dyad was generally healthier than the patient acting alone, or at least their comments appeared to be healthier. The other issue at hand was that when we switched circles, those who had been in the supportive role found a tremendous job in perspective. They often said that they did not realize what the patient had to contend with until they entered that arena themselves.

Regardless of type, group interaction contains a mystery, which is probably based on a form of communication we have yet to scientifically demonstrate. But one can sense the magic in the circle. The term magic implies a level of communication that is deeper than the individual egos of members of the group.

References

Dayton, T. & Moreno, Z. (2004). *The living stage: A step-by-step guide to psychodrama, sociometry and group psychotherapy (paperback edition).* Deerfield Beach, FL: HCI Books.

Lean, G. (1989). *On the tail of a comet: The life of Frank Buchman.* Colorado Springs, CO: Helmers & Howard Publishers.

Schutz, W. (1973). *Elements of encounter.* New York: Harper & Row.

Wikipedia.org (2015). *Erhard seminar training.* From: Cults: Faith, Healing, and Coercion, by Marc Galanter (1999). New York: Oxford University Press.

Wollert, R., Levy, L, & Knight, B. (1982). Help-Giving in Behavioral Control and Stress Coping Self-Help Groups. *Small Group Research. 13*(2): 204 – 218.

Yalom, I. (1995). *The theory and practice of group psychotherapy (fourth edition).* New York: Basic Books.

Chapter II

Personality: A Group Perspective

"The idea of contribution is especially instructive because
it lies in the area that unites the 'I' and the 'we'.
We contribute because we are part of something larger than our own
lives and efforts, but the form of our contribution
is based on our uniqueness and our individuality."
– Carol Ochs (American author)

Many of us are too frequently frantic and more than just a bit anxious about issues over which we have no control. Ordinary folks who have no obvious malady are apt to smoke like a chimney or eat doughnuts to obesity feel a lessening of tension and anxiety when consuming vast quantities of whatever. As mentioned earlier we come into the world with a unique personality, which is magically crammed into a tiny chromosome in the form of a gene. Identical twins separated at birth are often found to be nearly identical in many personality features. What do you guess is the need or reason for personality and why does it remain so entrenched after years of different environments? We have to ask ourselves what is the purpose of personality? Is being so different from one another really good if it also makes us feel alone? With all the well-conducted twin studies that we have available, it is safe to say that there is a tremendous store of information within the genes, which will be unleashed on the world at the time of our birth.

Chess and Freud

Though many a cringing parent knows the stereotypical "terrible twos", Chess and Thomas in 1977 demonstrated striking differences in babies at birth in the form of easy babies, slow to warm up babies, and difficult babies. Dr. Stella Chess, with whom I had the honor to work at the Florida School for the Deaf and Blind (FSDB), was never properly credited with the impact of her discoveries on early child development. Without a doubt she countered Freud's notions about early childhood with clear and concise analysis of more than 130 children, which she carefully followed and documented from birth to adulthood. This empirical research study spanned more than twenty years. Meanwhile we have had decades of Freud's Oedipus complex because he sought to be a celebrity, was an excellent writer and had an ego that would fill a stadium. As reported in 2007 by Steven Miller, in the *New York Sun*, on the occasion of Dr. Chess' death at age 93:

In "Your Child Is a Person," they insisted, "Prevailing psychoanalytically based theories of child care are wrong." They (Chess and Thomas) went on to check off the list of Freudian pitfalls: toilet training, thumb sucking, and weaning. Rather than representing some kind of trauma, they wrote, each was a normal part of childhood development. Of toilet training, they wrote, "It seems incredible that a task accomplished routinely in most of the civilized and uncivilized world for a very long time could create so much worry in 20th century Americans."

Dr. Chess was an excellent writer but also a very humble and dedicated clinician. She was found dead in in her home at age 93 because she had not shown up for work in a week. She was willing to give help to me in working with multi-handicapped kids at the FSDB but would gain nothing from it. In personality she was extremely different from Sigmund Freud. Freud's showmanship and the condescending way he dealt with assumed enemies of his theories were in sharp contrast to the personality of Stella Chess and her husband and colleague, Alexander Thomas.

Personality is a profound arbiter of people's emotions and decision-making. Because of Freud's powerful personality, we have had decades of incorrect theories dominating the landscape of psychology and psychiatry. In the same vein, when considering the design of the supporting person group it was necessary to consider a powerful ego present in the group and the damage that could be done by such a power. But on the other hand, people coming into this group with damage to their personality have been greatly helped by the nature of the group and the response that we have seen in people with ego damage such as a childhood of emotional abuse.

Personality Theory

Personality is a very complex phenomenon. I suppose one could say that it is the bedrock of who we are; however, it is very difficult to define. Harry Stack Sullivan saw personality as the sum total of our interactions with other people. This is quite different from most other theorists and clinicians. But we are to some people quite different than we are to other people. It is often said that the children are practically revered by some outside the home but seen as villains within the home. How is it that we can be so different to our parents than we are to others? Stella Chess solved the baby's personality as roughly fitting into three basic types including the easy baby, the difficult baby, and the slow to warm up baby. My own take on the mystery is that I could not understand how our seven children could be so different from each other practically from day one. My wife made, I thought, an extreme effort to learn who her new baby was. She never imposed on the baby a personality trait that was not there. At about six weeks of age she would declare "now I know this baby". At the time I did not realize how important this issue was. It did not occur to me then that a phenomenon as complex as personality could be packed into tiny genes within the baby's chromosomes. But since then as we have come to know more and more about what we call evolutionary psychology the whole process makes more sense. Within families people may often remark that a child is just like his grandpa; however, we have no way of knowing whether the child might indeed bear similar traits to hundreds of ancestral grandpas before him. We are a genetic continuation of our forefathers.

But we spend a great deal of time and effort on notions that are handed down in the literature from prominent psychologists and psychiatrists. Watson and Skinner believed that when children are born they are a blank slate and can be molded and shaped into the desired child. Nothing could have been further from the truth but it tells the story and that story is that we will believe things that seem to look like they make sense but in actuality they make no sense at all. When I think about what research, is I think that much of it is looking at something over and over again until it finally fits together as a whole. We have been led through countless lectures and textbooks to believe Freudian nonsense. We have reviewed and taken exams and gotten 100% correct on veritable malarkey.

But what is personality for? What do we need of it? It may make more sense from the wide view of simply being a mammal than a human being. We know that some mammals, such as the seal and the penguin, the mother and father have to be able to find their young amidst a sea of others of their kind. How they do this remains a mystery. We all know that our fingerprints are different from each other and medical students know that the textbook of anatomy is only accurate for about 80 percent of the subjects involved. To digress a bit, I am reminded that my father was credited with discovering a lizard for which there is only one sex, the female. When asked why we have males in other species he said that the only strong probability was that we had males for diversity. So is the personality the driving principle of evolution? I believe it is certainly a central feature of life. How could we possibly have gotten this far along the path to the human being had it not been for diversity (often in the form of mutation but not necessarily only in the mutation)?

Personality and Psychiatry

Psychiatry is still somewhat underdeveloped as a medical science. We can't do lab tests or x-rays to diagnose a mental disorder. Our diagnoses are basically theories that describe particular constellations of behaviors and thought patterns over time as reported by patients or their families, subjectively for the most part; however, as a result of many years of psychological research, we know that people, if exposed to certain sets of adverse life circumstances, will have difficulty functioning. We can pretty much predict, based on someone's background, who may end up in psychiatric treatment, have marital or career problems, or bump up against the legal system. This doesn't mean that people don't have to take responsibility for what they do, but it does mean that we are to some extent products of our environment. The person's environment is dysfunctional, not the person. But the individual gets labeled as being crazy, sick, broken, or screwed up. This is stigmatizing and not so great for anyone's self-esteem, which makes people feel worse and compounds the problem.

We sometimes do people a disservice by labeling them with a mental disorder when in fact they have been functioning quite effectively at surviving under profoundly difficult life circumstances. In the U.S. health care system, psychiatric providers make diagnoses and prescribe medications because that's how we get paid. There are other ways to help people get better and heal their lives, but the system doesn't usually pay us to help people in those ways.

Personality has been described by some theorists as an individual's characteristics and tendencies that have continuity over time and are not easily explained solely as the result of social or biological influences. Personality also refers to the patterns of thoughts, feelings, social adjustments, and behaviors that a person consistently has that strongly influence their expectations, self-perceptions, values, and attitudes. It also predicts our reactions to other people, problems, and stressors.

Understanding our personality can be useful in evaluating our own needs related to family, career, or personal growth. An awareness of our personality traits can also help us better understand our motivations, desires, and unique way of being in the world that may be different from our friends, romantic partners, or co-workers. Personality traits are simply what a person is like. A description of one's personality does not diagnose or pathologize human behavior. No prescription is required.

Personalities within a Group

Being in a group and seeing the similarities and differences between others and ourselves can help us understand ourselves, our relationships, and our world a little better. Groups can serve as a support network and a sounding board. Other members of the group can help us come up with specific ideas for improving difficult situations or life challenges.

Regularly talking and listening to others also helps us to put our own problems in perspective. You may sometimes feel like you're the only one struggling, but you're not. It can be a relief to hear others discuss what they're going through and realize that you're not alone.

Diversity is another important benefit of being in a group, because people have different personalities and backgrounds and they tend to look at situations in different ways. By seeing how other people tackle problems and make positive changes, a person can discover a whole range of new strategies for facing their own concerns.

Genetics and Personality – A Tribute

I'd like to share some thoughts about Frieda Springer. She carried a gift in her genes, which she in turn bestowed to her children, and thence, her grandchildren. It is the gift of discovery. She did not mold or shape her seven babies. I know because I was there. She discovered them in every nuance of their emerging personalities.

It was a joy to watch and listen. Some mothers want their babies to behave in certain ways. Frieda sought to bring out the personality she knew was there. She did not force bonding but carefully recognized each facet of the baby's personality as it unfolded. I know I was remiss in enjoying the process so much. But it was so real and so worth repeating over and over. She intuitively knew what was happening. I was simply in awe. These mother-baby moments might have been captured but like all the other aspects of her life, the essential emotion is the essence. The emotion of the moment passes on, hopefully to the next generation.

References

Chess, S. & Thomas, A, (1995). *Temperament in clinical practice.* New York: Guilford Press.

Kazantzakis, N. & Wildman, C. (1953). *Zorba the Greek.* New York: Simon and Schuster.

Miller, S. (20 March 2007). Obituary of Stella Chess, 93, psychiatrist and author. *New York Sun.*

Skinner, B. (1965). *Science and human behavior.* New York: Free Press.

Sullivan, H. (1953). *The interpersonal theory of psychiatry.* New York: W.W. Norton & Company.

Watson, J. (1970). *Behaviorism.* New York: W.W. Norton & Company.

Chapter III

How Have the Professionals Failed Us?

"What if conversation is how things get done?"
– Juanita Brown (co-founder of the
World Café conversational process)

It is perhaps too strong a remark to say that psychiatry and psychology have failed us. Much of the problem lies within our economy and how the economics of life drives all other things to sometimes-grotesque proportions. Just as we fail as a culture to put early childhood education and nurturance at the top of our list, we also fail to see how important early childhood nurturance is. We need look at the prisons, the mentally ill, and even those who have chosen homelessness is a way of life. What we do know is our knowledge of early childhood is just now emerging. We have hopefully transcended the Watson and Skinner era and now see the baby in a more realistic light.

The fact of historical acceleration certainly does not give much time for reflection and review. As parents we were only a little more than twenty years ahead of the children that we reared. In that twenty year time span, we have been going through countless revisions in our thinking about a variety of basic issues. I remember a time when I thought my grandparents knew nothing of the present but a great deal about the past. The question is whether we are going through history in such an accelerated fashion and the casualties are so numerous that we become numb to reality. So we now have a culture, which is replete with the casualties of war, disease, and our inhumanity to each other. The Supportive Person Group Process can be a tool in our ability to deal with such a rampant culture of alienation as we have.

Insurance Reimbursement and DSM Diagnoses

One could easily say that third-party reimbursement in insurance matters has caused a great deal of trouble for both psychology and psychiatry. With the advent of the *American Psychiatric Association's Diagnostic and Statistical Manual of Mental Disorders (DSM-III)*, there was an attempt to restructure diagnosis so that it would fall into the general medical arena and thence be carried along with the appropriate diagnoses and treatments based on the clinician's ability to keep up with these matters. But we moved rapidly from that area to DSM-IV and then to DSM-V. The move from DSM-IV to DSM-V has been fought by psychiatrist Allen Frances and others.

Frances warned that *"the expanding boundary of psychiatry is causing a diagnostic inflation that is swallowing up normality, and the over-treatment of the worried well is distracting attention from psychiatry's core mission of treating the more severely ill"*. Frances pointed out that mislabeling everyday problems as mental disorders has serious implications for individuals and society. The stigmatization of a healthy person as mentally ill can lead to the use of unnecessary and potentially harmful treatments, the misallocation of clinical resources, and the depletion of the budgets of families and our country.

Furthermore, this trend has the effect of shifting the responsibility for our psychological well-being away from our own naturally resilient, self-healing brains, which have been keeping human beings sane for hundreds of thousands of years, into the hands of a corporate pharmaceutical industry that is reaping multi-billion-dollar profits every year.

Frances also pointed out that "psychiatric diagnosis still relies exclusively on fallible subjective judgments rather than objective biological tests". Regardless of which side you take concerning the DSM-V, it is apparent that something has not worked out right.

Child Psychiatry and the DSM

Now I must digress a bit. When I was a resident completing my tour of three years, it became apparent to me that something went dreadfully missing. Some residents moved directly into child psychiatry. At the time I wondered whether they were choosing this to become child psychiatrists or was it something else. I learned over the years that many of them did not become child psychiatrists, or they focused on it for only a part of their practice. They knew based on things I overlooked that the three-year psychiatry residency was totally devoid of the issue of child development and childhood mental illness. Because of their work in the residency in child psychiatry, they were much better suited to deal with the issues as they arose in their individual patients. Also, in my opinion, there is a paucity of child psychiatrists within the DSM revision process. I believe that child psychiatrists would have developed diagnoses based partly at least on developmental issues.

There are many patients now who profess to have both bipolar disorder and schizophrenia because there was no clarity conveyed to them as to what their problem was and how their psychiatrist arrived at a diagnosis. At least the drug companies are happy because additional diagnoses, no matter what the basis is, fall into the commercial thrust that comes up with the brand new medications for the new diagnoses. But what do we really know about ourselves that will help us, no matter what the diagnosis, to find more peace and be more effective as a human being? Certainly we are left with many questions when trying to make sense of modern psychiatric nomenclature:

Doctor, what do I really have? Can I be cured? What can I do for myself? I know you conducted an evaluation but when you shared the results with me I was left without knowing any more than when I came in.

In a 15-minute medication visit by a psychiatrist, nothing will be accomplished except that the psychiatrist must use words of caution concerning the medication because of fear of being sued. He or she does not have time to concern himself with the patient's true nature or true concerns but has plugged the patient into a diagnosis for which no real explanation given to the individual. It is a dreadful impasse to say the least. It is not that there is or has been a true conspiracy but it turned out that the drug companies and insurance companies shared a common desire. Both wanted to have a fixed diagnosis for which to render their brand of psychiatric servicing. As time has gone on, it has gotten only worse.

The Pharmaceutical Industry

Dr. Harriet Fraad, a mental health counselor, believes that the pharmaceutical industry has manufactured a "climate of insanity" by manipulating and even creating illness for financial gain. Fraad wrote that "one of the things that drives Big Pharma is to find a diagnosis that is very vague, so that everybody can fall into it."

Fraad further pointed out that everybody is sad sometimes for good reasons. The point of Big Pharma is to market pharmaceuticals. Their advertising strategy is to have vague diagnoses and then find "wiggle room" so that they apply to everyone. Psycho-pharmaceuticals may actually be less effective for many people, in the long run, than talk therapy. Talk therapy, like drugs, can change our brain and body chemistry, and it has fewer side effects than medications. Talk therapy provides people with tools that can usually help to solve future problems.

The use of widespread bipolar diagnoses and bipolar mood-stabilizing medications is an example of how market-driven mental health care works in the United States, according to Fraad. It illustrates the transformation of health care into a system dominated by some of the wealthiest corporations in the world. Fraad believes that caring about profit is first, and that is why psychiatry has turned to drug therapy. Antipsychotic medications alone (not including medications for anxiety and depression) net the pharmaceutical industry approximately 14 billion dollars per year. Fraad reported that psychotropic medications are the most profitable sector of the industry, which makes it one of the most profitable business sectors in the world. Americans are less than five percent of the world's population, yet we consume 66 percent of the world's psychiatric medications. Although studies suggest that talk therapy may be as good as or better than drugs in the treatment of depression, fewer than half of depressed patients now get such therapy compared with the vast majority twenty years ago.

Neuroscience: We are Hard-Wired to Connect

According to Amy Banks, MD, neuroscience research confirms that our nervous systems are hard-wired to connect with other human beings. Scientists who use advanced imaging technology (fMRI) to study brain function report that the human brain is wired for caring and cooperation. According to this research, just thinking about another person experiencing harm can trigger the same reaction in our brain as when a mother sees distress in her infant's face. Conversely, the act of helping another person triggers the brain's pleasure center and benefits our health by boosting our immune system, reducing our heart rate, and preparing us to approach and soothe. Positive emotions like compassion can produce similar benefits. Conversely, negative emotions can suppress our immune system, increase our heart rate, and prepare us for fight or flight.

According to David Korten, these finding are consistent with the feelings of pleasure most people experience from being a member of an effective team or lending a helping hand to another person in need. If our brains were not wired for life in community, our species would have become extinct long ago. We have an instinctual desire to protect our group. Behavior contrary to this positive norm is an indicator of social and psychological dysfunction. The supportive person group process can help people connect and begin to move in more positive directions.

References

Allen, F. (6 August 2013). "The new crisis of confidence in psychiatric diagnosis". *Annals of Internal Medicine, 159(2)*: 221–222.

Allen, F. (2014). *Saving normal: An insider's revolt against out-of-control psychiatric diagnosis, DSM-5, Big Pharma, and the medicalization of ordinary life.* New York: William Morrow Paperbacks.

American Psychiatric Association (2013). *Diagnostic and statistical manual of mental disorders 5th edition (DSM-V).* Arlington, VA: American Psychiatric Publishing.

Banks, A. (15 September 2010). *Humans are hardwired for connection.* Wellesley Centers for Women. https://www.wcwonline.org/

Fraad, H. (15 March 2011). Profiting from mental ill-health. *The Guardian.*

Korten, D. (30 July 2008). We are hard-wired to care and connect. *Yes Magazine.*

Skinner, B. (1965). *Science and human behavior.* New York: Free Press.

Watson, J. (1970). *Behaviorism.* New York: W.W. Norton & Company.

Chapter IV

How Does Alcoholics Anonymous Compare With Other Treatments?

"I do not go to a meeting merely to give my own ideas. If that were all, I might write my fellow members a letter. But neither do I go simply to learn other people's ideas. If that were all, I might ask each to write me a letter. I go to a meeting in order that all together we may create a group idea, an idea which will be better than all of our ideas added together. For this group idea will not be produced by any process of addition, but by the interpenetration of us all." - Mary Parker Follett (American social worker)

Although I came into Alcoholics Anonymous more than thirty years ago, I continued to come to meetings sporadically and hesitantly for at least 10 years without any sense of the gravity and inherent beauty of the 12 Steps. In my early years with AA, the meetings had the honesty of naiveté, in my way of thinking, rather than the informed truth of enlightenment. How wrong I was and how arrogant was my thinking. Actually, in my training in medicine, only one professor (Arthur Guyton) reached out to students with the simplest of explanations and found us not lacking but found his own approach often not clear enough for many students.

Dr. Guyton, a polio survivor, strikes me as a bottom-up teacher. From Wikipedia I have extracted a paragraph distilling the concept of bottom up processing:

*"A **bottom-up** approach is the piecing together of systems to give rise to more complex systems, thus making the original systems subsystems of the emergent system. Bottom-up processing is a type of information processing based on incoming data from the environment*

to form a perception. From a cognitive psychology perspective, information enters the eyes in one direction (sensory input, or the "bottom"), and is then turned into an image by the brain that can be interpreted and recognized as a perception (output that is "built up" from processing to final cognition). In a bottom-up approach the individual base elements of the system are first specified in great detail. These elements are then linked together to form larger subsystems, which then in turn are linked, sometimes in many levels, until a complete top-level system is formed. This strategy often resembles a "seed" model, whereby the beginnings are small but eventually grow in complexity and completeness."

Dr. Guyton would go over and over teaching material until we all understood it. He would take complex physiology to its simplest form and build on the material from the ground up.

There are two amazing issues within Alcoholics Anonymous that appear to have arisen ahead of their time. I believe these issues have kept AA in the grillwork rather than the tail lights of history for at least the past 70 years. The first issue is that AA sees the field of play as the group, whereas psychology and psychiatry have made the individual not only the field of play but also, because of economics, the only way reimbursement could be handled. AA had no such encumbrance since remuneration is secondary and voluntary. Meanwhile, confidence in group process in AA has grown while individual therapy by a psychiatrist is now reaching a whopping $300.00 per hour. The cost of 30 antipsychotic pills (Abilify – name brand) is between $750 and $1000.

Returning to review the efforts made to deal with mental infirmity and addiction from 1906 with the Emmanuel Movement forward, it is clear that there was underestimation of the problem as the leaders of the movement frequently used hypnosis as a means of helping an alcoholic. The Emmanuel Movement was a psychologically-based approach to religious healing that was provided as an outreach program of the Emmanuel Church in Boston, Massachusetts.

Also at issue, but also the underlying fault, was the misidentification of the problem of alcoholism as a simple spiritual problem. Alcoholism is both a physical illness and a spiritual malady as well. Looking back, it now appears that the efforts made were in good faith but were lacking in the eventual enlightenment of the revolution in discovery of the nature and scope of the tiny genome. In the study of genetics we find that alcoholism has a partial causality within the genome, but there is also the interaction with the environment that completes the picture. But now that science has zeroed in on the genome, what lies ahead? We are on a journey to discover how our genes play tag with our environment. We are learning that even our intestinal bacteria influence our health, and how we think can influence our genes. In the words of Satchel Paige, the philosopher-baseball player: "Don't look back they may be gaining on you."

While science is dealing with the minutia of the living genome, many in AA are diving straight into the heart of their own conundrum. Why do they continue to study daily the picky issues of their personality and relationships with others though sober for many years? Why not just go home and watch TV or mow the yard? Many churches offer the top-down approach and avoid open discussion of sin and character defects in an open forum. Is it because they are looking ahead for something more than sobriety? We can be thankful there is a lot of bottom-up processing going on in the countless meetings of AA all over the world. In *Not God: A History of Alcoholics Anonymous*, Ernest Kurtz writes:

Arthur Cain, in two articles in 1963 (Harper's) and 1965 (Saturday Evening Post), offered less restrained criticism. In an opening paragraph that reflected the pomposity he found in Alcoholics Anonymous, the Columbia-trained psychologist flayed "a movement which is becoming one of America's most fanatical religious cults: 'A.A.'" Cain expatiated on his "religious" critique by accusing Alcoholics Anonymous of being "anti-science," "intolerant," "dogmatic," and even of having its own "Holy Grail ('the actual coffee pot Anne used to make the first A.A. coffee')" and more. "The cake and coffee served after meetings are just refreshments, not the body and blood of Jesus Christ."

In my own 30-plus years of attending AA meetings, I have seen no evidence that AA is a religion or a cult. But some observers offer a lame criticism that AA is both a cult and a religion. Though many people who go to AA are seeking God, some clerics and church leaders lay claim from a top-down methodology to have found God on our behalf and some are sneakier than others in their effort to solve our problem with death and the threat of finality. As a card-carrying

(Social Security card) octogenarian, I know that some religions try and fail to offer redemption in exchange for allegiance.

When Bill Wilson was meeting with Bishop Fulton Sheen on a regular basis with the idea of becoming a Roman Catholic, Bill W. finally backed away on the issue of the infallibility of the pope. He simply could not accept that a human being was infallible, although he made a valiant attempt to become Catholic.

According to religion historian Karen Armstrong, Freud regarded God as an illusion, based on the infantile need for a powerful father figure. Religion, Armstrong explained, which was necessary to help early humans restrain their violent impulses during the development of civilization, can now be set aside in favor of reason and science; however, in my own humble opinion, science can become just as oppressive as religion and has been for centuries. The notion that reason can hold water for very long is also not acceptable to me. In 1970, Bill Wilson went to the grave with a "seeking attitude" toward God. This, to me, is true humility and allows one to be open to better things in the future. In his most recent book, *The Meaning of Human Existence*, Edward O. Wilson (no relation to Bill Wilson) tells us that science should not seek to dispose of the humanities. He gloms the arts and religion into one, which he calls the humanities:

"Science and the humanities, it is true, are fundamentally different from each other in what they say and do. But they are complementary to each other in origin, and they arise from the same creative processes in the human brain. If the heuristic and analytic power of science can be joined with the introspective creativity of the humanities, human existence will rise to an infinitely more productive and interesting meaning."

At least Edward O. Wilson had the humility to admit that science is of human invention because it arises out of our brain as opposed to some science buffs who see science as coming to us, sweeping out of a wise cosmos and enveloping us humans in the vastness of it all. Although some researchers such as the Cochrane Collective argue that there is a lack of evidence on the effectiveness of 12-step groups, Dr. Lee Ann Kaskutas, a scientist in the Alcohol Research Department at the University of California Berkeley School of Public Health, found that, in a focused literature review of AA effectiveness (as opposed to formal treatment):

- Rates of abstinence are twice as high among those who attend AA.
- Higher levels of attendance are associated with higher rates of abstinence.
- Prior AA attendance is predictive of subsequent abstinence.
- Mechanisms of action predicted by theories of behavior change are present in AA.

In this study, the above relationships and outcomes were found for different samples of AA members in a variety of settings and follow-up intervals over time. The goal of the study was not to provide an exhaustive review of the evidence, but rather to present representative studies that address AA effectiveness in accordance with accepted criteria for establishing scientific cause and effect, including magnitude of effect, plausibility, and consistency of effect.

The title of Chapter IX implies that all treatment modalities in human history comprise religion as treatment modalities, as well as modern psychology and psychiatry. Certainly the mentally ill were cared for within religious organizations prior to Freud's bursting onto the scene. Although in the past decade or so, secular or humanist AA groups have become more common, seven of twelve steps refer either to a deity, such as God or Higher Power (greater than oneself), or to religious practices such as prayer. The ultimate goal of sobriety, as the final step states, is to achieve a spiritual awakening, and the Serenity Prayer is a staple of AA meetings.

But when someone is trying to stop drinking, it is the peer support aspect of AA groups that can be an invaluable source of guidance, assistance, and encouragement. Groups are very helpful, not only in maintaining sobriety, but also as a safe milieu where people can discuss challenges and receive support. Connecting with others who understand firsthand what an individual is going through can help reduce feelings of isolation, hopelessness, and fear. Staying motivated and positive is much easier when there are supportive people to turn to and lean on during tough times.

Meyer Maskin spoke of psychoanalysis in the context of modern advertising as "your cure could be just one interpretation away". He also had mentioned on hearing of the budget that was projected (in the 1980s) for the mental health needs for Putnam County, Florida as ludicrous, and he suggested that it would make as much sense to simply use some local crop-dusters to spray the county with Valium. The dollar figure in his mind was so miniscule compared to the true need that the crop-duster solution was as rational and achievable as anything else.

What AA meetings have done for Putnam County and all of the counties and provinces around the world cannot be reasonably estimated in dollars or any other currency. Simply put, when you go to a psychiatrist's or psychologist's office or a mental health clinic, you expect to be fixed or at least given relief through a currency or a co-pay arrangement, but when you attend an AA meeting you are essentially given a shovel and advised to start digging. The fall-out of positive effects on the family of alcoholics cannot be easily estimated, but the message that the alcoholic brings home to his for her family is simple and direct as opposed to the message brought home from psychiatrist and psychotherapist, which is often clouded in secrecy and fuzzy nomenclature. In the case of Alcoholics Anonymous, there is a spawning of vast networks of Adult Children of Alcoholics, Alanon, Narcotics Anonymous, etc. Many other copycat support groups are well known, and are growing in number and effectiveness. These groups in general have not altered the 12 Steps and 12 Traditions in their literature, and therefore cohesiveness is transposed among the groups. From my perspective as a psychiatrist and a member of a self-help group for more than three decades, it makes sense to build upon what works and to strengthen the weaker links wherever possible.

To many alcoholics who have had several years of AA experience, their lament is the claim that they sat for several years in AA meetings without active participation. In other words, they did not seek a sponsor and did not actively study the 12 Steps, nor did they share their experience in a meeting. To quite a few, only frequent relapse led to getting a sponsor or studying the AA literature or sharing in meetings. Seeking psychotherapy for one's ills is often too little and too late to be effective but the AA alternative requires, as a rule, intense and prolonged effort.

References

Armstrong, K. (1993). *A history of God.* New York: Ballantine Books.

Cain, A. (19 September 1964*).* "Alcoholics can be cured - Despite A.A." *Saturday Evening Post.*

Kaskutas, L. (2009). Alcoholics Anonymous effectiveness: Faith meets science.

Journal of Addiction Diseases, 28(2): 145 – 157.

Kurtz, E. (2010). *Not God: A history of Alcoholics Anonymous.* Center City, MN: Hazelden Publishing.

Maskin, M. (1989). *Wisdom and wit: A collection of papers.* Portsmouth, NH: P. E. Randall Publisher.

Wikipedia (2015). *Top down and bottom up design.* https://en.wikipedia.org

Wilson, B. (1955). *Alcoholics Anonymous: The story of how many thousands of men and women have recovered from alcoholism.* New York: Alcoholics Anonymous Publishing.

Wilson, E. (2014). *The meaning of human existence.* New York: Liveright Publications.

Chapter V

The Supportive Person Concept

"The individuals in great dyads will be very different from each other and very much alike. These simultaneous extremist generate the deep rapport and energizing friction to define a creating a pair." – J.W. Shenk (from The Power of Two)
"Since we cannot change reality, let us change the eyes which see reality." - Nikos Kazantzakis (author of Zorba the Greek)

The essential difference in the supportive person group concept and the historical well-known group therapy concept is that two people are required to get to know each other at some modest level before the group even begins. One can be the mouthpiece in the inner circle while the other is observing what is going on. The observing one can be very helpful and letting the person in the inner circle know more about his environment. As he gets to know his supportive person, he will be able to be of assistance in making the points within the inner circle group. The outer circle person should rarely speak spontaneously, but may be invited to speak on behalf of the inner circle person. When the groups reverse their position a similar pattern continues until they reach compatibility and effectiveness. In our modern society, we are processing a great deal of information on a minute-to-minute basis. It would be rare to have two people who are totally similar to each other. Their contrasting views give energy to the group.

The pair generally arouses more intense energy than an individual in a group. What has then been found in prior instances is that the outer circle person finds it very difficult to remain silent and sometimes interrupts the entire group session in order to make a point. Because of the energy involved, it is not always a bad thing when this

31

happens. Once this happens, the inner circle person is more apt to engage his group in dialogue. When one considers the variety of personalities in the group as a whole, as well as the intensity level of the two personalities within the dyad, it is easy to see why this group is much more powerful than typical therapy groups or even encounter groups.

The Dyad Defined

What exactly is a dyad? A dyad consists of two people. It is the smallest possible social group. A dyadic relationship is the dynamic that is generated between two individuals who are interacting with one another. A dyad can be unstable, because both people have to cooperate in order to make it work. If one or the other fails to complete their duties, the dyad will fall apart. The pair of individuals in a dyad could be linked by friendship, common interests, work, or other factors. They may even be partners in crime.

Dyadic communication refers to the inter-relationship between the two individuals. This relationship involves dialogue or face-to-face verbal communication between two people involving their mutual ideas, concerns, interests, and maybe even answers to questions about the meaning of life. This is the nucleus of social conversations.

Brief, random communications between two strangers on the street and not continued afterwards, or not having any lasting effect on either person, cannot be considered to be dyadic communication. An example of dyadic communication would be the biblical relationship between Jesus and Peter, where conversation is not merely mechanical or superficial, but instead develops connection and support and brings the dyad into a sphere where each member influences the other. Dyadic communication involves the sharing of ideas in a way that achieves an enduring and deep impact on the pair.

According to Shenk, "From what I've seen time and again, the essential seed for how two people to not only support each other but also to startle and vex each other, leading to daring work that neither could achieve alone." He goes on to say that "Put another way, the individuals in great dyads will be very different from each other and very much alike. These simultaneous extremes generate the deep rapport and energizing friction that define the creative pair". Shenk quotes psychologist Diana McLain Smith as follows: "The two people who have the most creative potential are the people who are the most different. The question is how do they harness that difference in the service of creatively instead of cancelling each other out?"

The most common concern that I have heard as two people are approaching the idea of the supporting person is the fear that they do not know the other individual well enough and it would take a great deal of time and effort to get to know one another. This is in sharp contrast to something I learned from the book *Blink* by Malcolm Gladwell. He contends, and I agree with him, that *"Snap judgments are, first of all, enormously quick: they rely on the thinnest slices of experience. But they are also unconscious."*

The concept of thin-slicing is not foreign to the field of psychotherapy. John Gottman, a well-known expert in marriage counseling, describes how within an hour of observing a couple, he can predict with 95% accuracy whether the couple will be together in 15 years. His accuracy is about 90% if he observes the couples for only 15 minutes, supporting the phenomenon of thin-slicing.

In brief therapy, which focuses on a specific problem rather than a lengthy analysis of the history of a patient's distress, the goal is to find a quick solution to a problem or complaint. Psychologist Richard Bandler explains that *"It's easier to cure a phobia in ten minutes than in five years. The speed with which you do things makes them last. I taught people the phobia cure. They'd do part of it one week, part of it the next, and part of it the week after. Then they'd come to me and say 'It doesn't work!' If, however, you do it in five minutes, and repeat it till it happens very fast, the brain understands. That's part of how the brain learns. I discovered that the human mind does not learn slowly. It learns quickly."*

Practicing one's role as a supportive person will at least give an individual the opportunity to strengthen their confidence in quick decisions. It can also help people develop more awareness and confidence in trusting their own unconscious mind.

When the SPGP circles are reversed, a sudden shift in awareness of each other's intent and sincerity may come about. This is a true demonstration of how a person can change through a change in perspective as a result of the insights and power of dyadic one-to-one conversations within the group.

References

Bandler, R. (1993). *Time for a change*. Cupertino, CA: Meta Publications.

Gladwell, M. (2007). *Blink: The power of thinking without thinking*. New York: Back Bay Books.

Gottman, J. (1995). *Why marriages succeed or fail: And how you can make yours last*. New York: Simon & Schuster.

Macionis, J. & Gerber, L. (2011). *Sociology. 7th edition*. Toronto: Pearson Prentice Hall.

Shenk, J. (2015). *The power of two: How relationships drive creativity*. New York: Eamon Dolan/Mariner Books.

Chapter VI

Unraveling the Mystery of the Double Circle

"We listened, and through that listening a dynamic of its own developed. The end result was a group spirit and group coherence stronger than any I have ever known, yet it was a dance with many dancers, a group of individuals who had found an emergent reality drawing our differences into a meaningful whole."
- Danah Zohar and Ian Marshall (from The Quantum Society)

One can easily wonder if double circle groups have always existed. We know that in early tribal times, the elders were generally in the inner circle of a big group of tribal affairs. It is easy enough to imagine that the rest of the tribe was standing back in the outer part of the circle trying to discover what the elders were all about. To the best of my knowledge, there is no historical account that provides any clues as to a double circle formal group process. I have searched the literature on this topic and found it wanting. Even though I began this work in 1978, there has been no report in the literature of any double circle groups to this day.

Dyads Within the Group

The mystery that I have experienced in many group sessions with the double circle is there was a feeling of intense energy coming from behind me while I was in the inner circle. I know that in other circumstances when I have felt the presence of another person behind me, and once I knew what their intent was I became more comfortable and more at ease. This feeling of intense energy coming from behind the inner circle is at first a bit frightening and intimidating. As time goes on, the tension has eased but the energy appears to remain. To me, the essential mystery is that the double circle group lights up and

35

glows (metaphorically speaking) with the intensity of the shared energy.

Sharing Our Stories

Although our stories and experiences are all different, people have many common themes that describe what it means to be human. As human beings, we're imperfect and flawed, we tend to make bad decisions, and we struggle to cope with life. Each person is unique, but we are still one in the same. It is through our sameness that we can connect and relate to one another. By listening to another's story, we learn more not only about that individual, but also more about ourselves. The dyadic relationships within the double circle group allow enhancement of this experience by giving members of the pair an opportunity to take turns understanding each other through mutual sharing and listening, exploring one another's points of view, and establishing rapport.

Humans are naturally social creatures. We're hard wired for relatedness, and our energy comes from connecting with others. When creating a connection, it can seem frightening at first, but it is our relationships with one another that help us grow and develop a rich, meaningful life. We want to be seen, welcomed, and appreciated in an environment of safety, acceptance, and loving kindness. We want to be able to speak our truth to one another.

Taking the First Step

One of the biggest reasons that people fear reaching out and connecting with others in social situations is that they don't know what to say, and they think they'll look like an idiot, according to Scott Dinsmore. He recommends a strategy called the three second rule. This strategy can be quite effective in an organized group setting, or it could also be a powerful pickup tool for any guy or girl who is looking to fall in love. If you see someone interesting or whom you want to meet, give yourself three seconds to walk up to that person and begin a conversation. If you wait any longer, you will either overthink the situation and mess things up, or you'll overthink it and never say anything at all.

Don't worry about what to say, Dinsmore recommends. The content of the first conversation is not particularly important.

Anything is better than nothing. Once you speak a word to someone, you're immediately elevated out of the ocean of thousands of lonely bystanders, to the few who actually reach out to connect, and this is a huge first step.

Nevertheless, when starting a double circle group, it is important to address participants' expectations about the why, what, and how of the group experience, as this can help to alleviate any initial fears and discomforts that people might have. Encouraging people to be aware of their thoughts and feelings can help them move into the dyadic relationship, thus making the group function more effectively. Jumping into the double circle experience without any preparation or orientation may not yield optimal results. Explaining how it works can help people feel comfortable with the process of opening up to a dyadic partner, becoming vulnerable, and appreciating the intimacy and growing affection that can develop through their interactions.

Conventional Group Therapy

One of the difficulties about group therapy in its conventional configuration is that it is difficult to comprehend all the things that are simultaneously happening on many different levels. Given that the usual group has about 8 to 10 people, it is no small matter to keep up with the names of the participants, the basic issues expressed, and the overall mood of a cohort of group members. However, with the double circle group, the outer circle participants can draw their attention to the nature of the discussion, the moods of the participants, and the flow of energy within the group. If one were to imagine just a single circle, it is difficult to keep up with all of these dynamic features that are going on as a group participates in its work. The person who is in the inner circle being supported by his counterpart in the outer circle gains additional eyes and ears, or heightened awareness, with which to be better able to feel comfortable about what is going on.

Campfires and Storytelling

Tens of thousands of years ago early humans in primitive cultures sat around a campfire and the tribe lived as one community. We are no longer able to do this today, due to mass immigration, mobility, industrialization, and disconnectedness in our society. We can sit around a campfire, as did those indigenous people, but they were connected among themselves in a natural way, while we need to connect at a much deeper level below our egos that control us.

Native American teacher Whisper Panther writes that as a culture, we have mostly lost the experience of sharing our stories around the campfire or any other circle of community. But the need still remains. It is through the contemplation of our shared stories that we interpret and integrate our experiences. This is how we evolve. She explains that it can be a touching experience when people from the modern world are brought into circles of connection and expression of community. The group experience allows people to find their voices and build interdependence and friendship within the group. Hearing each other's stories helps us pave new thought patterns that can breathe new life into stale ways of being, stretch us beyond our old mental habits that no longer serve us, and help us re-prioritize our values and identify what is truly important.

The Mystery

To unravel the mystery of the double circle, the word that comes to mind more than any other word is perspective. But what do we mean by perspective? To me, perspective is a realization through a change in position in an entirely different view as a result of what is going on in the group. According to Robert Wicks, *"When someone gains or regains a healthy sense of perspective, it feels like pure magic. The person sees more clearly and experiences greater freedom. Unforeseen possibility surfaces, and new peace and joy are seeded."*

Each time the circles reverse, a new portal of perspective opens. What had not been seen before is now seen with great clarity. Henry J.M. Nouwen asks in the Genesee Diary: *"Is there a quiet stream underneath the fluctuating affirmations and rejections of my little world? Is there a still point where my life is anchored and from which I can reach out with hope and courage and confidence?"*

The mystery of the double circle gradually fades away as one experiences the feeling of being in the outer circle and then changing to the inner circle. Each time I have made this change from inner to outer circle, I have been amazed by the effect it has on my way of seeing things.

References

Dinsmore, S. (2015). *Five underused tactics to make an immediate, genuine connection with anyone.* Brazen Careerist Blog. http://www.brazencareerist.com/blog

Nouwen, H. (1981). *The Genesee diary.* Colorado Springs, CO: Image Publishing.

Panther, W. (2015). *Freeing our indigenous soul.* http://www.crossingworlds.com

Wicks, Robert J. (2014). *Perspective: The calm within the storm.* New York: Oxford University Press.

Chapter VII

Why Have Support Groups?

"Practical intelligence includes things like "knowing what to say to whom, knowing when to say it, and knowing how to say it for maximum effect." - Robert Sternberg (American psychologist)

"Each person holds so much power within themselves that needs to be let out. Sometimes they just need a little nudge, a little direction, a little support, a little coaching, and the greatest things can happen."
- Pete Carroll (Head Coach of the Seattle Seahawks)

The most striking thing that I learned at the National Training Labs (NTL) in Bethel, Maine was that there is an essential difference between a committee and a group. It turned out to be at least a very healthy difference, because I always disliked committees before that. I found that when a group is really effective, each person who speaks is attempting to make the group better rather than simply making himself look better and more powerful. In the committee, the dominant male usually commands and all others agree or disagree and often a free-for-all ensues. Order is maintained by the strict dominance of the committee chairman.

In a group, the leader can best be a facilitator of what the group is trying to do; however, the group must first find itself through a gradual development of inclusion, which is the way in which each member decides how and why he feels included in this particular group. The next phase, which is going on simultaneously, is establishing where the controls lie. This can be a very complex process. Finally, when inclusion and control are settled comfortably something that is called affection evolves. This affection cannot be found in a committee unless the committee has made a conscious decision to become a group. This would take a very wise committee chairman and that is hardly ever the case.

Support groups are generally information filters. They filter information that comes in from the media and other sources and reach a consensus about this information that is satisfactory to the group. It is definitely a bottom-up versus a top-down activity. In our recent history, we've seen the proliferation of information particularly via the television medium, which is often based on an effort to sell something. This process leads to a great deal of misinformation. The support group is quite effective in filtering out the misinformation and giving testimony to the effectiveness of something that at least several people in the group have experienced.

Peacemaking Circles

One type of support group that has recently been developed arose out of a need for conflict resolution in schools. The technique has carried over into use in restorative justice as well. The *Little Book of Circle Processes* describes this phenomenon, stating that peacemaking circles provide a way to bring people together to hold difficult conversations such as working through conflicts or differences. This process is a means of getting the most complete picture individuals can have of themselves, one another, and the particular issues at hand. The circles are based on an assumption of positive potential and hope that something good can always come out of whatever situation we are in. This enables people to move together in a good way.

Peacemaking circles also assume that none of us alone has the total picture. It is only by sharing all of our perspectives that we can come closer to seeing the complete picture. Sharing our individual perspectives and knowledge creates a collective wisdom that is much greater than the sum of its parts.

Restorative Justice Groups

Restorative justice is an approach to justice that focuses on the needs of victims and offenders, as well as the involved community, rather than merely satisfying abstract legal principles and punishing the offender. Victims are given an active role in the process, and offenders are encouraged to take responsibility for their actions, as well as repair the harm they've done by apologizing, returning stolen property or money, or doing community service. It also provides help for the offender in order to avoid repeat offenses. The process of restorative justice necessitates a shift in responsibility for addressing crime. In a restorative justice process, the citizens who have been affected by a crime must be willing to take an active role in addressing that crime.

Restorative justice is based on a theory of justice that considers crime and wrongdoing to be an offense against an individual or community, rather than the state. It fosters dialogue between victim and offender, and reportedly provides significant rates of victim satisfaction and offender accountability. Proponents of restorative justice believe that all stakeholders impacted by an injustice should have the opportunity to discuss how they have been affected by the situation and to decide what should be done to fix the problem. With regard to criminal activity, restorative justice is about the idea that because a crime hurts people, justice should heal. It follows that conversations with those who have been hurt and with those who have inflicted the harm are important in the healing process. Restorative justice seeks to expand the issues beyond those that are legally relevant, especially into the underlying relationships between the affected members of the community.

Kay Pranis describes a group process in which participants arrange themselves in a circle and pass a talking piece (stick) around the circle to assure that each individual has an opportunity to speak, one at a time, in the order in which they are seated within the group. A philosophy or set of values is often articulated as part of this process. These values generally emphasize respect, the worth and dignity of each participant, integrity, and the importance of speaking from the heart. One or two circle keepers serve as facilitators.

Pranis points out that in indigenous communities the elders play an important role in leading the group or in offering advice and insights. Circles consciously enlarge their circle of participants. Victims, family members, offenders, justice officials and court personnel are included, but other members of the community are essential participants as well. Sometimes these community members are invited to attend because of their connections to or interest in the specific crime or the offender and/or the victim, but sometimes they are simply part of an ongoing circle of volunteers from the community.

According to Howard Zehr, group process is emerging in the criminal justice system because it is more effective in dealing with conflict than conventional justice programs. It is effective because it is a bottom-up method for dealing with criminal behavior. Support groups can bring responsibility and repayment to all of the participants in the community. So we are moving toward support groups in a variety of settings.

The process of restorative justice aims to bring about a shift in responsibility for addressing the problem of crime. In a restorative justice process, the community members who have been affected by a crime engage in doing most of the work of addressing the problem. Although law professionals also may play a role in facilitating the restorative justice process, it is the citizens who must assume most of the responsibility for healing the pain caused by breaking the law. Zehr states that in restorative justice groups, the following questions should be addressed:

- Who has been hurt?
- What are their needs?
- Whose obligations are these?
- What are the causes?
- Who has a stake in the situation?
- What is the appropriate process to involve stakeholders in an effort to address the cause of the problem and make things right?

The process of restorative justice creates a huge shift in responsibility for addressing crime and other social problems through the development of community support. The groups promote communication, reconciliation, connection, and the rebuilding of relationships within the community. This has been a growing social movement since the 1990s and shows promise in establishing peaceful, mutually supportive, group approaches to harm, criminal behavior, and violations of legal and human rights around the world, in the United Kingdom, Brazil, Canada, and the United States, not only within criminal justice systems, but also in schools, social service organizations, and communities as a whole.

Collective Consciousness

Asking why we need support groups is like asking why we need our unconscious memories from ancient tribal times. The collective unconscious is a powerful form of internal knowing common to humankind that originates in the inherited structures of the brain. It is believed to contain universal images and ideas accumulated from the experiences of previous generations. It influences our desires and behaviors, even when we are not aware.

Similarly, collective consciousness refers to how we view ourselves as part of a group, sharing mutual knowledge, understanding, and support, as individual members of a larger group or cohesive whole. In the absence of connectedness to other members of our human tribe, our very existence would be at risk; therefore, groups are valuable and important in order for individuals and communities to survive and thrive.

References

Braithwaite, J. (2002). *Restorative justice and responsive regulation.* New York: Oxford University Press.

Pranis, K. (2015). *Little book of circle processes: A new/old approach to peacemaking* (Little Books of Justice & Peacebuilding) (Kindle Locations 849-854). Good Books. Kindle Edition.

Price, M. (2000). "Personalizing crime". *Dispute Resolution Magazine* 7(1): 8–11.

Zehr, H. (2015). *The little book of restorative justice: Revised and updated* (Justice and Peacebuilding) (Kindle Locations 658-666). Good Books. Kindle Edition.

Chapter VIII

Evolution of Human Group Relationships

"Life is not a solo act. It's a huge collaboration, and we all need to assemble around us the people who care about us and support us in times of strife." - Tim Gunn (American actor)

Evolutionary psychology is a form of social science that looks at our mental processes from an evolutionary point of view. Its primary interest is in basic human nature and finding commonalities among people as well as seeking to understand why people have many diverse types of personality traits.

The theory on which evolutionary psychology is based began with Darwin's work, including his ideas about the origins of human social instincts. Evolutionary psychologists say that natural selection has provided humans with many psychological adaptations, similar to the way in which physical adaptations have gradually come about over many thousands of years.

According to evolutionary psychologists, our behavior is a result of psychological adjustments our ancestors learned to make long ago in order to solve problems in their environment related to mating, parenting, and belonging to social groups.

Some of our personality traits and preferences can be understood in terms of the survival value they held for early humans. Certain characteristics may have survived because the genes they're linked to were "selected" and became part of our heritage. For example, we may tend to find nature scenes appealing because, for our ancestors, they represented elements needed for survival. Think of lush green vegetation, trees laden with fruits and nuts, or crystal clear rivers and streams.

Similarly, humans have a tendency to seek wealth and power because in prehistoric times such assets increased their chances of surviving and enhanced their reproductive possibilities. The human instinct to wage war is strong because ancient tribes of genetically similar people lived in constant competition with others.

Social Evolution

Edward O. Wilson offers another interesting view on the evolution of human social behavior, focusing on cooperation and altruism rather than competing and conquering. As the brain size of early African humans increased through evolution, these ancient beings developed increased intelligence through vastly improved memory. This allowed humans to make use of the detailed knowledge of each member of their group, as opposed to relying primarily on instinct-driven behaviors; therefore, social organization became increasingly important. According to Wilson, the origin of our human condition is best explained by natural selection for social interaction. Our inherited tendency to communicate, cooperate, and bond with one another brings about deep satisfaction of belonging to our own special social group. Social intelligence enhanced by group selection has made humans the first fully dominant species in the history of our planet.

The Selfish Gene

Social evolution arises from the sum of all interactions of each individual with every other member of the group. There are two levels of natural selection - individual and group. Selfish members may win within a group, but groups of unselfish or altruistic people tend to trump groups of selfish members. Richard Dawkins argues in *The Selfish Gene* that natural selection has favored genes that cooperate with others. In fierce competition for scarce resources, there's a premium on central coordination rather than anarchy within a communal body. For instance, a member of a group who is a successful thief looks out for his own selfish interests, but his behavior weakens the rest of the group. When a brave warrior leads his group to victory in a battle, even if he is killed, the rest of the group benefits from his heroism.

Tribal Circles

We believe that the tribal circles of our ancestors have meaning today, although they are buried within our genetic material and require some effort to recapture their power. Such groups are still highly relevant for our lives in the modern world. Eckhart Tolle believes that we have outrun our brain's capacity to deal with many of life's problems because our collective and individual egos have run well ahead of our emotional capacity to deal with each other. Returning to small group interaction may help us regain our footing. But this is a slow evolving process and requires intelligent effort.

Now multiply this example by dozens or hundreds of similar examples, influencing all aspects of our bodies, minds, and societies, and you will begin to appreciate the need to think of ourselves as a product of evolution, just like any other species. A good recent book on this topic is *Strangers to Ourselves: Discovering the Adaptive Unconscious,* by social psychologist Timothy Wilson, who shows us how many of our decisions are driven by unconscious algorithms similar to fetuses "deciding" their metabolic strategy.

According to David Sloan Wilson, "We have not escaped evolution. We experience evolution at warp speed. The starship Evolution is not like the starship Enterprise, however. Unless we understand how it works, it will take us to places that we don't want to go."

In many of our current job situations, CEOs and managers set up policies that are based on their collective imaginations but unfortunately not on our evolving capacities or any understanding of the evolving nature of human intelligence and emotion. We are not included in the process, and so it is always from the top down rather than the more intelligent way of from the bottom up.

The Hundredth Monkey

The mechanism by which evolutionary change takes place within groups may be something like the "hundredth monkey" effect. In this phenomenon, a new idea or behavior can spread quickly from one group to other related groups once a critical number of members adopt the new practice or acknowledges the novel idea. The story was made popular by Ken Keys, Jr. in his book *The Hundredth Monkey.*

The story claimed that it was based on the observations of Japanese scientists, who observed macaque monkeys on the island of Koshima in the 1950s. They supposedly observed that some of the monkeys learned to wash sweet potatoes, and this new habit gradually spread to a younger generation of monkeys. Once the hundredth monkey learned the new habit, according to the story, it spread to other populations of monkeys on nearby islands.

Whether or not this research is valid, we know that tipping points like the hundredth monkey concept can exist. Keys may have written the story of the hundredth monkey effect as a hypothetical tale of inspiration, applying it to human society to instill a vision of effecting change.

The Tipping Point

A tipping point is defined as a moment in time when a group, or a significant portion of a population, makes a rapid and dramatic behavioral change by widely adopting a previously rare behavior or idea. The term was made popular as it applies to daily life by Malcolm Gladwell's book *The Tipping Point: How Little Things Can Make a Big Difference*.

According to Gladwell, a tipping point is "a magic moment when an idea, trend, or social behavior crosses a threshold, tips, and spreads like wildfire". Tipping points do not always bring about immediate positive change but may be the beginning of a resolution to a significant social problem. Labor strikes, mass migrations, revolutions, and riots are the results of tipping points. These occurrences may be difficult to predict or anticipate, but when the conditions are right and critical mass has been reached, they happen. This often resembles a bottom-up "seed" model, in which the beginnings are small but can grow over time in complexity and completeness.

References

Dawkins, R. (1976). *The selfish gene.* New York: Oxford University Press.

Gladwell, M. (2002). *The tipping point: How little things can make a big difference.* New York: Back Bay Books.

Keys, K. (1982). *The hundredth monkey*. New Delhi, India: Vision Books.

Tolle, E. (2004). *The power of now: A guide to spiritual enlightenment.* Vancouver, BC: Namaste Publishing.

Wilson, D. (2007). *Evolution for everyone: How Darwin's theory can change the way we think about our lives.* New York: Random House.

Wilson, E. (2014). *The meaning of human existence.* New York: Liveright Publications.

Wilson, T. (2004). *Strangers to ourselves: Discovering the adaptive unconscious.* Cambridge, MA: Belknap Press.

Chapter IX

Let's Not Throw the Baby (Spirituality) Out With the Bathwater

"Rhetoric is the art of discourse, an art that aims to improve the capability of writers or speakers to inform, persuade, or motivate particular audiences in specific situations."
- Edward Corbett (American author)

It is not unlikely that soon the Supreme Court would have hotel and motel owners place a copy of Dawkins book, *The God Delusion*, alongside the Bible. Meanwhile, rhetoric continues concerning the evidence for God, the rationale for God, and the history of the whole mess. Richard Dawkins believes that he has made a compelling argument for doing away with God. He does so without any apparent concern for the noise that such a vacuum would create. For whatever reason, I have not spoken to God as Moses did, according to the Bible, but I do feel it is my duty to search for God, and doing so, be given more clues as to what my role should be in taking care of this planet and any others that we might leave debris upon. If religion is the opiate of the masses, as Marx had suggested a number of years ago, it is certainly been a 10,000 year trip plus or minus a few thousand years. As psychiatrist Bob Baringer suggested, we are tripping on our own juices. What we perceive as "the divine" may actually be neurochemical reactions in our brain. Sometimes when we experience emotions like joy, awe, and ecstasy we call it "God" or "spirituality" depending on the circumstances and how we're interpreting what's going on in our environment. But some of our religious experiences may be like a "trip" or getting high on endorphins, dopamine, or other neurotransmitters.

Psychiatry and spirituality share the common language of distress and despair, as well as the mutual goals of hope and good health. Nevertheless, religion and psychotherapy have never been very tight. Freud saw religion as pathological. Religious Americans, especially fundamentalist Christians, tend to view psychotherapy as a hallmark of secular America, alienated from any religious influence, according to Scott Richards, author of the book *Spiritual Strategy for Counseling and Psychotherapy*.

Not only was Freud an atheist, but behaviorists such as Watson and Skinner who came afterwards were also eager to avoid religion in order to establish psychology as a respected scientific discipline. As a result, psychotherapists have generally considered the subject of religion to be taboo in their practices.

Pamela Paul reported in 2005 that nearly three-fourths of Americans say their whole approach to life is based on religion. In a recent study conducted by the Pew Research Center, about 70 percent of Americans reported belonging to the Christian faith; however, only about thirty percent of psychiatrists and psychologists report being religious, according to Paul, an apostle of Jesus. This may result in some people feeling more comfortable seeking help outside of the traditional psychological because mental health professionals tend to be less devout than the general population.

Many traditional counselor education programs offer little or no training in dealing with spiritual matters. Yet many people prefer counselors who share their religious beliefs and support rather than challenge their faith. Religious people may fear that secular therapists will view their faith as a problem or a symptom, rather than as a philosophy to be respected and integrated into therapy. Many Americans believe that their spirituality and religious beliefs are closely tied to their mental and emotional health; therefore it is important for a professional counselor to honor their values and beliefs within the counseling process. Some people would prefer to see a religious counselor than a psychiatrist, psychologist, or family doctor.

Religion and Spirituality

It should be pointed out that some people identify themselves as being spiritual but not religious. According to Robert Fuller, author of the book *Spiritual but Not Religious*, confusion exists about the differences between these two concepts. Both words imply a belief in some sort of higher power and a desire for connection with that power, and both may involve an interest in rituals or practices, moral behavior, and ethical living. We are being spiritual whenever we are moved by values such as love, beauty, and creativity, which seem to reveal a power beyond the visible world. Spiritual issues include wondering what happens when we die, where the universe comes from, and why we are here. Spirituality exists whenever we try to figure out the meaning of life and how we fit into the greater scheme of things.

Spirituality is generally more closely linked with alternate philosophies and exploring the purpose of life. It may or may not involve engaging in specific practices such as prayer or meditation. It involves our inner thoughts and personal experiences, whereas religion is associated with membership in a church or other formal religious organization or denomination.

The relationship between spirituality and religion was further addressed by Emmet Fox in his book *Sermon on the Mount*. In this book, he clearly shows that Jesus was not of the church but of the people. He expresses that in many different ways, but the significant thing is how Jesus is from the "bottom-up" type of people in history. This is also true of Paul; however, in contrast, much of what we hear from the Pope is "top-down" philosophy.

According to Harold Koenig, spirituality, as opposed to religion, is an inner capacity, consciousness, or state of awareness. It is a process of personal growth or a journey that can provide the motivating drive for living. Koenig feels that spirituality is more difficult to define. Because it is more personal, it is largely free of rules and regulations, whereas religion is sometimes viewed as being divisive and associated with conflict and war.

Stanislav Grof, a founder of the transpersonal psychology movement, which integrates spirituality and transcendence within mainstream psychology, wrote that "the toll for the loss of spirituality is an impoverished, alienated, and unfulfilling way of life and an increase of emotional disorders." According to Grof, "It is in the interest of all of us to find ways of bringing spirituality back into our individual and collective lives." This would include recognizing spirituality as an essential part of human existence. An important aspect of this effort would the development of a support system for people undergoing a spiritual or emotional crisis. This is because spirituality can create a new sense of engagement and commitment to reconciliation and transforming relationships.

Addiction and Spirituality

Furthermore, it makes sense to describe alcoholism and addiction as forms of psycho-spiritual crisis or spiritual emergency. In substance abuse, the spiritual dimension is obscured by the self-destructive nature of the disease. In addictions, according to Grof, the source of the problem is a strong spiritual longing and the absence of connection to others, the divine, and something greater than oneself.

There is plenty of evidence that beneath the craving for drugs or alcohol is an unrecognized craving for transcendence or wholeness, according to Grof. Many people in recovery talk about their restless search for an unknown missing element or dimension in their lives. They describe unfulfilling and frustrating pursuits of substances, food, relationships, possessions, or power that reflects an unrelenting effort to satisfy their cravings.

One way of understanding addiction might be to consider that similarity exists between mystical states and intoxication by alcohol or drugs, according to Grof. Both of these states share the feeling of dissolving individual boundaries, dissipating painful emotions, and a feeling of rising above or escaping from mundane problems. Although intoxication lacks some important characteristics of a mystical state, such as serenity and the richness of philosophical insights, the overlap of these experiences can be enough to entice alcoholics and addicts into abuse.

William James was aware of this connection, and wrote about it in *Varieties of Religious Experience*: "The sway of alcohol over mankind is unquestionably due to its power to stimulate the mystical faculties of human nature, usually crushed to earth by the cold facts and criticisms of the sober hour. Sobriety diminishes, discriminates, and says no; drunkenness expands, unites and says yes." James recommended religion as the best treatment for alcoholism.

Jung and Twelve Step Groups

Although it isn't widely known, Carl Jung played an important role in the history of Alcoholics Anonymous. Jung's insight was instrumental in developing the worldwide network of twelve-step programs. Information about this aspect of Jung's work can be found in a letter that Bill Wilson, the cofounder of AA, wrote to Jung in 1961 (Wilson and Jung, 1963). Jung had a patient, Roland H., who came to him after having exhausted other ways of recovering from alcoholism. Following a temporary improvement after a year of therapy with Jung, Roland suffered a relapse. Jung told him that his case was hopeless and suggested that his only chance was to join a religious community and hope for a spiritual experience. Roland joined the Oxford Group and experienced a religious conversion that freed him from alcoholism. He was able to help Bill Wilson's friend, Edwin T., who in turn helped Bill Wilson in his personal crisis. In a powerful spiritual experience, Bill Wilson reportedly had a vision of a worldwide network of fellowship circles of alcoholics supporting one another.

Many years later, Wilson wrote Jung a letter, in which he brought to his attention the important role that Jung played in the history of AA. In his answer, Jung wrote in reference to his patient: "His craving for alcohol was the equivalent, on a low level, of the spiritual thirst of our being for wholeness, expressed as "a union with God." Jung pointed out that in Latin, the term "spiritus" covers both meanings (alcohol and spirit). He again expressed his belief that only a deep spiritual experience can save people from the ravages of alcohol. The insights of Jung and James have subsequently been confirmed by the experiences of many people in twelve-step programs.

References

AA Grapevine (1963). *The Bill W. – Carl Jung letters.* http://silkworth.net

Buechner, F. (1991). *Telling secrets.* New York: Harper Collins.

Corbett, E. (1990). *Classical rhetoric for the modern student.* New York: Oxford University Press.

Dawkins, R. (2008). *The God delusion.* New York: Mariner Books.

Fox, E. (2009). *The sermon on the mount: The key to success in life.* New York: Harper One Publications.

Fuller, R. (2001). *Spiritual but not religious: Understanding unchurched America.* New York: Oxford University Press.

Grof, S. (1987). *Spirituality, addiction, and western Science.* Re–Vision Journal, 10, 5 - 18.

James, W. (1902). *Varieties of religious experience.* New York: Longmans, Green, & Company.

Jung, C. (1960). *Psychology and religion.* New Haven, CT: Yale University Press.

Koenig, H. (2009). Research on religion, spirituality, and mental health: A review. *Canadian Journal of Psychiatry, 54*(5), 283 – 291.

Paul, P. (1 May 2005). With God as my shrink. *Psychology Today.* https://www.psychologytoday.com

Richards, P. & Bergin, A. (2005). *Spiritual strategy for counseling and psychotherapy.* Washington, DC: American Psychological Association.

Skinner, B. (1965). *Science and human behavior.* New York: Free Press.

Watson, J. (1970). *Behaviorism.* New York: W.W. Norton & Company.

Chapter X

SPGP Procedures:
The Instrument

"When we focus on clarifying what is being observed, felt, and needed rather than on diagnosing and judging, we discover the depth of our own compassion."
- Marshall Rosenberg (American psychologist)

This chapter focuses on the procedures and guidelines for conducting the group. It is important to point out that the SPGP groups are not psychotherapy groups, nor are they a treatment for any type of mental disorder. They are designed to be led by non-professionals. The purpose of SPGP groups is self-help, or enrichment for depleted souls. The SPGP groups can enhance an individual's personal growth, sort of like weight lifting to help develop the mind. The SPGP can be very useful in teaching group process and can be helpful as a participant's or lay leader's first group experience.

The group may meet weekly or biweekly, or at some other interval as selected by the participants. The sessions generally last about an hour. The group can choose to meet for a specific number of sessions or indefinitely.

In the group meetings, the participants' chairs are typically placed in a circle so that participants can see one another. Half of the participants are seated in the inner circle, and the other half are seated behind them in the outer circle, just behind their right shoulders.

Again, we must stress that the scope of the SPGP is limited to personal growth, which might include improving communication skills, changing one's perceptions, and learning to connect better with others. The process can be used by non-professionals, and the group is appropriate for any educational level. The Twelve Steps would not be applicable for the SPGP, as the steps are intended to help people overcome a specific malady (addiction). The SPGP is not designed to diagnose or treat any psychiatric condition.

As previously explained in other chapters, when I was an Assistant Professor of Psychiatry at the University of Florida, I came to believe that it was important to provide group psychotherapy as a part of the inpatient experience. I initially used a large single circle, but I found that the medical students had a tendency to put the patients in an awkward position of having to defend themselves in the group. So I put the staff members and students in an outer circle behind the patients, and the patients had the inner circle with the group leader, generally myself. This helped to balance the power differential between the medical students and the psychiatric patients. It helped the medical students learn the delicate process of being supportive instead of meddling in the patients' business or otherwise putting the patients on the defensive. It also helped the students develop the ability to accept, validate, and be supportive of the patients in the manner that the patients understood themselves. The development of rapport, communication, and social intimacy within the pairs facilitates the mutually supportive role.

In the beginning, some or all of the members of a group may be complete strangers to one another. Being in dyads helps the participants get to know each other. In some cases, before rapport has developed among members, it may be necessary for the group leader or director to moderate the process at first, otherwise participants may sit in embarrassed and anxious silence.

The group session begins with a quiet conversation, lasting about ten minutes, between the inner circle participants and their respective supportive persons. It may be difficult to break off the conversation, because it's generally more comfortable to talk in a one-to-one relationship than it is to speak to a group. The shifting of the perspective from the dyads to the entire group and then back to the one-on-one conversations is crucial to the uniqueness of the SPGP. The group leader should remind participants that the group will be returning to the one-to-one discussions throughout the session in order to infuse new energy into the process and allow participants to breathe easily for a while.

While the session is in progress, the supportive person does not speak without the approval of their inner circle counterpart, or at least without tacit permission to speak on the other person's behalf when the group is meeting as a whole. The individual in the inner circle can evaluate whether or not what the supportive person says is true or helpful. So a great deal has to be worked out between the supportive person and the inner circle participant during the dyadic interactions.

Metaphorically speaking, one can see the inner circle as the engine and the outer circle as a supercharger of the engine. The main goal of the supercharger is to move the group in a more effective and intense manner than one would typically see in a regular self-help group. The outer circle provides energy and coaches the group toward increased engagement, cohesiveness, and self-disclosure.

The next step in the SPGP is to reverse the circles so that the outer circle participants are in the inner circle, and the others move to the outer circle to support or just listen to whatever inner circle members wish to share. They generally talk about the process of coming to understand what the other individual is like and how to be supportive of him or her. Participants become aware of how easy it is to be intrusive or just meddle in the other person's business rather than being supportive. It may be helpful, upon returning to the original configuration of the group, to reflect on participants' impressions of what happened within the periods of one-to-one interaction. Group members generally become aware of the importance of empathic support for their partner, in contrast to conducting an examination of the person's life.

Over time, group members can be encouraged not only to get to know each other better, but also to help others present problems in the group sessions that they may initially feel are too personal to voice. Participants can be role models to fellow group members by sharing their own personal experiences as well. During their turn as the supportive person, participants can often help their partner find a way to present an issue with both clarity and ease. The individual in the inner circle can express what they expect in a supportive person as well.

Group Introduction

The following is an introduction that can be used at the beginning of a Double Circle group meeting. It can be read at the start of each meeting for newcomers as well as those who are still trying to decide how the group should continue to be conducted: *"This group process method is not intended as therapy but as a way to achieve emotional and spiritual growth. The essence of this group is in the configuration of a single circle re-forming into a double circle and variations on the theme of the double circle. There is no diagnosis, malady, or addiction required to be a member of this group. The only requirement is a desire to gain insight into yourself as well as understanding and compassion for members of the group and other people in your life."*

The single circle formation at the beginning of a group meeting can be used as a time for focusing or a short meditation as well as dealing with any unfinished business or concerns from previous meetings. This should be relatively brief in order to devote most of the session to the *double circle mystery*. The simplest way to move into the double circle formation is simply to count off "one, two, one, two" and each person is assigned either the odd or even number. By convention, the "ones" become the inner circle and the "twos" become the outer circle.

By consensus, the individuals in the inner and outer circles will reverse positions periodically throughout the session. If the group has an odd number of participants, the extra person can be designated as the director or facilitator. This individual should pay attention the group's interactions, taking note of the duration of the dyads' conversations and when the circles should reverse positions.

Due to the decades of success brought to us by the Twelve Steps and Twelve Traditions of Alcoholics Anonymous, it is suggested that the group might incorporate them into the introduction process or opening words. According to the Hazelden Betty Ford Foundation, everyone can benefit from the wisdom of the AA philosophy (recovering alcoholics and non-alcoholics alike). It can help people learn to acknowledge their mistakes when they happen, repair any damage they may have done, learn humility, become less angry and resentful, and improve their relationships with others.

Psychologist Jerry Hirschfield wrote that the Twelve Steps are helpful for anyone who is seeking a practical path to spiritual growth and emotional freedom.

Check-in Procedure

Sometimes it may work well to have an open-ended discussion within the group, but at other times it may be necessary for the leader to provide a discussion topic in order to help the group focus and generate meaningful exchanges. The group leader or facilitator can use the check-in process at the beginning of the group meeting to accomplish this. In this process, the leader gives a brief introduction or description of the selected topic to help the entire group get centered, and then asks a guiding question or gives some simple instructions for sharing, including a sense of time. Two minutes per person is usually adequate for a check-in.

Check-in is not a time for casual conversation. It is a time for connecting. If a member hears something during check-in that they wish to talk to a fellow group member about, provide time at a break or the end of the meeting for that. The leader should keep in mind a polite but clear reminder to participants who go on a little bit too long.

A guided check-in can be a great way to break the ice, stimulate focused discussion, and help people to feel comfortable with each other. The group leader should invite participants to share briefly anything going on in their lives that they might wish to acknowledge in order to be more fully present in the group and in the moment. When starting the group with a check-in, participants in the group share in sequence (prior to teaming up in dyads), without questions or comments from other members. The facilitator generally goes first.

Check-in can be especially effective because it introduces a specific focus rather just than a vague "how are you?" that may not help people engage effectively with one another. A focused check-in process can also provide subsequent content for group discussions.

The use of a guiding or intentional check-in question at the beginning of a session can help the group go deeper by inviting creative interchange and encouraging connections between the work of the group and the personal growth of individual members. The leader should allow a brief period of silence for participants to reflect on the question and then give each person a minute or two to share his or her response. Following the silent reflection, invite group sharing, and then share any insights with the entire group as well as within the dyads.

Check-out Procedure

Doing a brief check-out at the end of group sessions gives participants a chance to wrap up any loose ends and get closure on the group discussion so that important things are not left unsaid. It can also be a time to briefly express appreciations for the sharing and connections that have occurred during the group session.

The FIRO

According to the Fundamental Interpersonal Relations Orientation (FIRO) theory, which seeks to explain the interpersonal underworld of a small group, when people get together in a group setting they are looking to fulfill three main interpersonal needs: inclusion, affection, and control. Psychologist William Schutz (whose 1967 book *Joy: Expanding Human Awareness* made encounter groups famous) developed the FIRO theory to measure how group members feel when it comes to personality traits such as their wanted or expressed need for control, level of sociability, rebelliousness, inhibition, flexibility, openness, warmth, and cautiousness. Groups provide an environment where participants can receive valuable, constructive feedback about others' perceptions of them, allowing individuals to see themselves through the eyes of their peers and gain new insights about their own personalities. It is hoped that the time needed to reach this stage will be remarkably shortened and improved in quality through the use of dyads in the SPGP method.

References

Hazelden Betty Ford Foundation (2015). *Twelve step recovery wisdom can benefit everyone.* www.hazelden.org

Hirschfield, J. (1987). *Twelve steps for everyone who really wants them.* Center City, MN: Hazelden Publishing.

Schutz, W. (1967). *Joy: Expanding human awareness.* New York: Grove Press.

Chapter XI

Special Populations and Future Research

"If you don't think your anxiety, depression, sadness and stress impact your physical health, think again. All of these emotions trigger chemical reactions in your body, which can lead to inflammation and a weakened immune system. Learn how to cope, dear friend. There will always be dark days."
- Kris Carr –
(Author, wellness expert, and cancer survivor)

"Become like the sky (at sunrise). Take an axe to the prison wall. Escape. Walk out like someone suddenly born into color. Do it now."- Rumi (Sufi poet)

As I was riding with several correctional officers back from a recent fishing trip to Steinhatchee, Florida, I heard them talking about guns, rounds, and different types of loads. They thought I had drifted off to sleep during the drive, so their conversation was easy, unfettered, and very technical. They seemed to be in their element. I was struck by the intensity of their conversation and the knowledge they shared. They knew their guns and ammunition. It was obvious that they had all studied firearms extensively. But why bother focusing on firearms? How can that save them from economic disasters that may lie ahead in the coming years?

In my half-awake state, I began to ponder some parallels. For the past several years, I've been studying the supportive person group model as they have been studying firearms. Group process and guns are both instruments. Like knives and forks, they are waiting to be picked up and used for a particular task or goal. In self-help groups such as the SPGP, participants share problems with one another, with the common goal of nourishing the other members and helping to create safe space within the group.

Many people are experiencing moderate or high levels of stress, especially at work. Because of continuing global economic instability, concerns about money and job security are among the top sources of stress. Occupational stress can occur when a discrepancy exists between the demands of the workplace and an individual's ability to cope. Common stressors include excessive workloads, long working hours, isolation, difficult relationships with management, and lack of autonomy. If not handled properly, stress can become distress.

Certain types of work have special sets of stressors. The work of a prison correctional officer, for example, tends to be highly stressful. In contrast to other public safety professionals such as firefighters and the police, correctional officers rarely receive praise from the public for doing a good job. When correctional officers do make the news, it is usually because they have been assaulted or are being accused of abuse or other misconduct such as accepting bribes. Correctional officers are rarely acknowledged for their daily efforts to maintain care, custody, and control of the society's most violent outcasts, nor are they paid exceptionally well for their work.

The number of incarcerated individuals in the United States now exceeds two million. Nearly one-fourth of all the prisoners in the world are in the U.S. Our prisons and jails are in the news almost every day, and our criminal justice system is badly in need of reform. Our system of dealing with people who have broken the law is simply not sustainable. The costs are overwhelming. Our correctional institutions, as well as those who go behind bars each day to work in them, are in crisis.

Correctional officers have significantly higher rates of suicide than other groups of professionals. Some officers develop post-traumatic stress disorder (PTSD) during their careers. They have higher rates of substance abuse, depression, and divorce than the general population. Correctional officers even have a shorter life expectancy than others.

Occupational stress, resulting from constant exposure to fear, conflict, diseases, and unpleasant working conditions can take a toll on an officer's health and well-being, often resulting in long-term negative effects. The results of chronic unmanaged stress, such as bad decisions, poor coping ability, excessive anger, and emotional distress, are not always recognized immediately. Frequent conflicts with administration, lack of trust, and feeling alienated from most of society can contribute to breakdowns in physical and emotional resilience of correctional personnel over time. Sometimes there is little support from professional associations and labor unions.

Officers in prisons and jails need help coping with their impossible jobs. Stress increases their risk for heart disease, diabetes, and other health problems. The effects of stress also affect criminal justice systems through poor work performance, absenteeism, high employee turnover, and replacement costs of hiring and training new employees.

In addition to stress management techniques such as exercise and recreational activities, correctional officers can benefit from learning peer support skills. Friends, confidants, acquaintances, co-workers, relatives, spouses, and other companions can provide a social network that improves their quality of life and may even increase longevity. People who enjoy close relationships with friends and family receive emotional support that indirectly helps to sustain them in times of stress and crisis.

Although professional help from mental health providers or employee assistance programs may be necessary in some cases, we believe that the SPGP self-help group can be beneficial either as complementary to professional care or as a preventative measure. It may be difficult for some correctional officers, when they first start participating, to see a support group as being more than just fluff if they are unaccustomed to sharing their thoughts and feelings. As people become acclimated to the group, they generally become more comfortable with self-disclosure and articulating their problems. Being in a group with fellow correctional officers, who are familiar with correctional policies, are knowledgeable about the corrections industry, and understand the issues that adversely affect correctional officers and their families can be a tremendously valuable experience.

Future Research

Although the SPGP has been in existence since the 1970s, formal studies of its use with special populations have not yet been done. We are hoping to conduct a study using the SPGP with correctional officers in Region 2 of the Florida Department of

Corrections, encompassing the Starke, Lake Butler, and surrounding geographical areas. We anticipate that the correctional officer participants will have a wide variety of years of work experience, but rather homogenous personal backgrounds. Many grew up and still reside in small, rural, depressed economic areas where there are few job opportunities. In Florida, state prisons tend to be built in areas where a county gives a land grant to the state in order to provide jobs and other economic benefits for residents of that county. Within this context, correctional officers may be seen as having at least one advantage (or disadvantage) in life.

Although correctional officers have a unique set of stressors that are uncommon in the general population, we believe that studying the effects of the SPGP with this group may yield helpful data that could be generalized to other groups, such as school teachers, social workers, married couples, and others who typically live with stressors that are less extreme.

One limitation of our model may be the length of time (number of weeks or sessions) it can take for the dyads to develop as effective, cohesive pairs. This has not yet been clearly determined. We also do now know how difficult it may be to recruit groups of 12 or more volunteer participants who can meet regularly on an ongoing basis because of time constraints due to family obligations, working overtime, or having a second job in order to make ends meet. Nevertheless, we hope that our study of the SPGP with correctional staff will provide strong support for the efficacy of this model.

References

Cray, D. (2005). High stress, low glamour: Correctional officers struggle with workplace strains. *Center for Mindfulness in Corrections*, www.mindfulcorrections.org.

Johnson, O. (2013). Correctional suicides: Doing time takes its toll. *Corrections One*. www.correctionsone.com

Lasley, E. & McEwen, B. (2012). *The end of stress as we know it.* New York: Dana Press.

Chapter XII

Conclusion

There are two very important reasons for carrying out the Double Circle type of group process as opposed to a traditional single circle self-help or support group format. The first is that the shift back and forth in circles allows members to develop a broader sense of perspective about how group process works. The second reason is that this process provides an opportunity for those in the outer circle to act in support of their counterpart in the inner circle, and this can be extremely gratifying. The dyadic relationships allow for both participants to practice deep listening as well as experience being heard by a supportive person. The underlying rationale for the Double Circle group is that as the sessions are repeated the dyads become more successful in being supportive of each other with other participants benefiting as well by witnessing the interactions.

A third reason for engaging in the Double Circle process, as explained in previous chapters, is that people today are continually faced with a deluge of multimedia information coming down from the top. In order to maintain emotional freedom, healthy boundaries, and peace of mind, it is important to find ways to counter this situation through a bottom-up process. Not all of the information coming from the top is accurate or beneficial for us. The Double Circle group process is an instrument that can help people maintain balance in their lives to counter the heavy weight of government and giant corporations. As the corporate world grows stronger and more oppressive, support groups can be a powerful source of strength for individuals. We can get in touch with our own truth and inner knowledge by hearing the experiences and perspectives of friends and other supportive people. This bottom-up type of processing can help individuals come together at a grassroots level and build community, clarify their own values, and increase their sense of personal effectiveness and control over their lives.

We believe that the Double Circle can provide a roadmap for bringing people together in small groups in ways that can support their need for personal growth and belonging. The Supportive Person Group Process is a bottom-up, grassroots movement that uses a group format to share and affirm our human experiences and help create connections. The Double Circle provides a unique and special setting in which we can process our experiences in today's fast-moving world, develop our listening skills, and build a trusting environment where we can be open and honest as well as care for others. This type of group can be used in a wide range of settings, including churches, hospitals, workplaces, schools, college campuses, neighborhoods, correctional facilities, assisted living homes, and community centers.

Noteworthy People

Armstrong, Karen - (born November 14, 1944) - British author of books on comparative religion. She is a former Roman Catholic nun, who went from a conservative to a more liberal and mystical Christian faith. She became disillusioned and left the convent in 1969. She earned a degree in English from St. Anne's College. Her work focuses on commonalities of the major religions, such as the importance of compassion and the Golden Rule. She first rose to prominence in 1993 with her book *A History of God: The 4000-Year Quest of Judaism, Christianity and Islam.*

Banks, Amy - American psychiatrist in private practice in Lexington, Massachusetts, specializing in psychopharmacology and relational therapy for patients who suffer from chronic disconnection issues. She has devoted her career to understanding the neurobiology of relationships.

In addition to her work at the Jean Baker Miller Training Institute (JBMTI), Dr. Banks has taught psychiatry at Harvard Medical School, and she is the first person to bring relational-cultural theory together with neuroscience, becoming an expert in this field. She created the C.A.R.E. Program, a practical guide that helps both clinicians and lay-people assess the quality of their relationships and strengthen their neural pathways for connection.

Baringer, Bob - American psychiatrist with whom Phil Springer conducted research for the National Institutes of Mental Health in 1958 while they were both medical students. They examined the role of ceruloplasmin in schizophrenia and conducted clinical research on LSD 25 for the Sandoz Pharmaceutical Company. Dr. Baringer is currently in private practice in St. Augustine, Florida, and also serves as the medical director of a detox center.

Cain, Arthur - British evolutionary biologist who claimed that AA is becoming one of America's most fanatical religious cults. He argued that AA is a useful idea that has turned into a hindrance to research and psychiatry because of its religious focus.

Chess, Stella - American child psychiatrist who investigated the individual styles of personality and temperament among children and discovered a method of identifying and rating nine separate "qualities" associated with personality and temperament.
The nine characteristics identified by Chess are:
    1.   the level and extent of motor activity
    2.   the rhythmicity, or degree of regularity, of functions such as eating, elimination, and the cycle of sleeping and wakefulness
    3.   the response to a new object or person, in terms of whether the child accepts the new experience or withdraws from it
    4.   the adaptability of behavior to changes in the environment
    5.   the threshold, or sensitivity, to stimuli
    6.   the intensity, or energy level, of responses
    7.   the child's general mood or "disposition", whether cheerful or given to crying, pleasant or cranky, friendly or unfriendly
    8.   the degree of the child's distractibility from what he is doing
    9.   the span of the child's attention and his persistence in an activity

Dinsmore, Scott - Entrepreneur, writer, former runner, and career change specialist. He describes himself as being on a mission "to change the world by helping people find what excites them and build a career around the work only they are capable of doing." Several years ago, a demoralizing experience at a Fortune 500 job launched Scott on a quest to understand why 80% of adults hate the work they do, and more importantly, to identify what the other 20% were doing differently.

Fraad, Harriet - Psychotherapist and hypnotherapist in New York City. She is a founding member of the feminist movement and the peer-reviewed sociology journal "*Rethinking Marxism.*" She is also a radical committed to helping people transform their personal and political lives in the United States.

Gladwell, Malcolm - (born September 3, 1963) - Journalist, author, and speaker on topics related to sociology, psychology, and social psychology. In his book *Blink*, he writes that it is quite possible for people who have never met us and who have spent only twenty minutes thinking about us to come to a better understanding of who we are than people who have known us for years. He also points out that if we are to learn to improve the quality of the decisions we make, we must accept the mysterious nature of our snap judgments, because there can be as much value in the blink of an eye as in months or rational analysis.

Gottman, John Mordecai - (born on April 26, 1942) - Professor emeritus in psychology at the University of Washington. He is known for his work on marital stability and relationship analysis through scientific direct observation, much of which has been published in peer-reviewed journals.
Gottman runs a non-profit research institute (The Relationship Research Institute) and a therapist training company called The Gottman Institute. He was recognized in 2007 as being one of the ten most influential therapists of the past quarter century. His research demonstrated that it isn't only how couples fight that mattered, but how they make up. Marriages are likely to become stable over time if couples can learn to reconcile successfully after a fight.

Grof, Stanislav - (born July 1, 1931) – Psychiatrist, one of the founders of the transpersonal psychology movement, and a researcher into the use of non-ordinary states of consciousness for purposes of exploring, healing, and obtaining growth and insights into the human psyche.

Guyton, Arthur Clifton - (September 8, 1919 – April 3, 2003) - American physiologist who later became Dean of the University of Mississippi School of Medicine. He is best known for his book

Textbook of Medical Physiology, which quickly became the standard text about the subject in medical schools. The first edition was published in 1956 and the 10th edition appeared in 2000, before Dr. Guyton died, and the 12th appeared in 2010. It is the world's best-selling physiology book and has been translated into 15 languages.

He was described as having an indomitable spirit. He suffered from polio but refused to succumb to its crippling effects. He sometimes walked long distances when using a wheelchair would have been easier.

Guyton's research contributions, including more than 40 books and 600 papers, place him among the greatest figures in the history of cardiovascular physiology. His research covered all parts of the cardiovascular system and led to many seminal concepts that became integral parts of the understanding of cardiovascular disorders.

Jung, Carl - German psychiatrist who influenced Bill Wilson, the founder of Alcoholics Anonymous. In correspondence, Jung wrote to Wilson that the cure for alcoholism would have to be a spiritual one, a power equal to the power of "spiritus" or alcohol. The 12 step programs emerged as that spiritual remedy. They outline a spiritual process of surrender of the ego to the unconscious, or a higher power, and resemble the process of transformation in Jungian psychotherapy.

Koenig, Harold G. - Psychiatrist who teaches at Duke University. His ideas regarding religion, spirituality, and health have been covered in Newsweek and other media, which are the focus of some of his research and clinical practice.

In a 2009 issue of *Newsweek*, comments by Koenig were featured, including his statement that he was "leading the charge for a better understanding of patients' religious and spiritual beliefs in the medical setting. It just makes too much sense, he said, when patient after patient tells him, Doctor, religion is the most important thing to me. It keeps me going." Koenig advocates that physicians should take the spiritual history of any patient with whom they are likely to have an ongoing therapeutic relationship, asking questions such as: "Is religion a source of comfort or stress? Do you have any religious beliefs that would influence your decision-making? Do you have any spiritual needs that someone should address?"

Korten, David - (born 1937) - American author, former professor of the Harvard Business School, critic of corporate globalization and political activist. He is also interested in psychology and behavioral systems. His best-known publication is *When Corporations Rule the World*. Korten's book *The Great Turning: From Empire to Earth Community* argues that the development of empires about 5000 years ago initiated unequal distribution of power and social benefits to the small portion of the population they controlled. He also argues that corporations are modern versions of empires, both being social organizations based on hierarchies and domination.

Meyer Maskin - American professor of psychiatry, a dear friend of Phil Springer, and was also colleague of Harry Stack Sullivan. He had a number of confrontations with Ernest Hemingway, and one in particular was the issue of mental illness claimed by Maskin and "fuck offs" claimed by Hemingway.

Nouwen, Henri Jozef Machiel - (born January 24, 1932) Dutch-born Catholic priest, professor, and writer. His interests were rooted primarily in psychology, pastoral ministry, spirituality, social justice, and community. Over the course of his life, Nouwen was heavily influenced by the works of Thomas Merton, Rembrandt, and Vincent van Gogh.
After twenty years of teaching at the University of Notre Dame, Yale Divinity School, and Harvard Divinity School, Nouwen began working with mentally and physically handicapped people at the L'Arche Daybreak community in Richmond Hill, Ontario. Nouwen authored 39 books and hundreds of articles. His books have sold million copies worldwide and have been published in more than 30 languages.

Paul, Pamela - Editor of the *New York Times Book Review* and former columnist for the *New York Times*. She testified on the subject of pornography before the U.S. Senate Judiciary Committee in 2005. She has appeared on television and radio shows in the U.S., Canada, and the UK, speaking about social trends. She has also spoken at conferences on the social costs of pornography and related topics.

Richards, P. Scott - American psychologist and author who teaches at Brigham Young University. He is also the Director of Research at the Center for Change in Orem, Utah. He co-authored *A Spiritual Strategy for Counseling and Psychotherapy,* which was the first book to provide guidance for integrating spiritual strategies into mainstream psychology. He is respectful of the scientific metho, and argues that spirituality can be studied scientifically.

Rosenberg, Marshall - (October 6, 1934 – February 7, 2015) - American psychologist and creator of nonviolent communication, a communication process that helps people exchange necessary information to resolve conflicts and differences peacefully. He was the founder and former Director of Educational Services for the Center for Nonviolent Communication, an international non-profit organization.

Schutz, William – (December 19, 1925 – November 9, 2002) - Psychologist who practiced at the Esalen Institute in the 1960s. He received his PhD from UCLA. He taught at Tufts University, Harvard University, University of California, Berkeley and the Albert Einstein College of Medicine. In the 1950s, he was part of a peer group at the University of Chicago's Counseling Center that included Carl Rogers and Abraham Maslow.

In 1958, Schutz introduced a theory of interpersonal relations he called Fundamental Interpersonal Relations Orientation (FIRO). According to the theory, three dimensions of interpersonal relations were deemed to be necessary and sufficient to explain most human interaction: inclusion, control, and affection. These dimensions have been widely used to assess group dynamics.

Sheen, Fulton John - (born Peter John Sheen, May 8, 1895 – December 9, 1979) - American archbishop of the Catholic Church known for his preaching and especially his work on television and radio. His cause for canonization as a saint was officially opened in

2002. In 2012, Pope Benedict XVI recognized a decree from the Congregation for the Causes of Saints, stating that Sheen lived a life of heroic virtues, a major step towards beatification, so he is now referred to as Venerable in the Catholic tradition.

Shenk, Joshua Wolf - Author of *The Powers of Two: How Relationships Drive Creativity*. He has also written articles for publications such as *The New Yorker, The New York Times, Slate,* and *The Nation*. His first book, *Lincoln's Melancholy*, won awards from The Abraham Lincoln Institute, the National Alliance for the Mentally Ill, and the National Mental Health Association.

Skinner, B. F. - (March 20, 1904 – August 18, 1990) - American psychologist who wrote *The Behavior of Organisms* and introduced the behavioral concepts of operant conditioning and shaping.

Smith, Diana - Senior partner at New Profit focusing on leadership transformation within its portfolio. Starting in 2010, Diana served as the firm's Chief Executive Partner for two years, working with the firm's leadership and staff to transform the culture and build a strong platform for growth. Prior to joining New Profit, Diana served as a partner and thought leader at the Monitor Group, a global management consultancy, and she is co-founder of Action Design, a firm that specializes in professional and organizational learning. She earned her master's and doctoral degrees in consulting psychology at Harvard University.

Sullivan, Harry Stack - (February 21, 1892 – January 14, 1949) - American Neo-Freudian psychiatrist and psychoanalyst who held that our personality lives within a complex system of interpersonal relations. Having studied therapists Sigmund Freud, Adolf Meyer, and William Alanson White, he devoted years of clinical and research work to helping people with psychotic disorders.
His writings include *The Interpersonal Theory of Psychiatry* (1953), *The Psychiatric Interview* (1954), *Conceptions of Modern Psychiatry* (1966), and *Schizophrenia as a Human Process* (1962). His book *Personal Psychopathology* (1972) contains a chapter on

male adolescence with extensive data on the interaction of sexual practices, personality development, and societal structures.

Tolle, Eckhart - (born February 16, 1948) - German-born author and spiritual teacher. Author of *The Power of Now* and *A New Earth*. He wrote that "Time isn't precious at all, because it is an illusion. What you perceive as precious is not time but the one point that is out of time: the Now. That is precious indeed." The more we focus on time, Tolle points out, such as the past or the future, the more we miss the present moment, which is the most precious thing in life.

Watson, John B. - (January 9, 1878 – September 25, 1958) - Psychologist who established the behavioral school of psychology (classical conditioning). He conducted research on behavior modification, primarily with children and animals.

Wicks, Robert J. - Psychologist who is widely known for helping to restore lives traumatized by massive tragedies such as the genocides that occurred in Rwanda and Cambodia. He regularly helps medical professionals and other aid workers, as well as men and women serving in the U.S. military.

Wilson, David Sloan - (born 1949) - American evolutionary biologist and distinguished professor of biological sciences and anthropology at Binghamton University. He is the son of the author Sloan Wilson. His book *Darwin's Cathedral* proposes that religion is a multilevel adaptation and a product of cultural evolution developed through a process of selection for cooperative and cohesive groups. His book *Evolution for Everyone: How Darwin's Theory Can Change the Way We Think About Our Lives* introduces evolution for a broad audience, detailing various ways in which it can be applied to everyday life. There is a course at Binghamton University called "Evolution for Everyone", and students are required to read the book as part of the curriculum.

Wilson, Edward Osborne "E. O." - (born June 10, 1929) - American biologist, researcher (sociobiology, biodiversity, island biogeography), theorist (consilience, biophilia), naturalist (conservationist), and author. His biological specialty is myrmecology, the study of ants, on which he is considered to be the world's leading expert.

Wilson is known for his scientific career, his role as the father of sociobiology and biodiversity, his environmental advocacy, and his secular-humanist and deist ideas pertaining to religious and ethical matters. Among his greatest contributions to ecological theory is the theory of island biogeography, which he developed in collaboration with mathematical ecologist Robert MacArthur. This theory is seen as the foundation of conservation area design, as well as the unified neutral theory of biodiversity.

Wilson, Timothy D. - American psychology professor at the University of Virginia. He is a social psychologist who researches the influence of the unconscious mind on preferences, behavior, and decision-making. His book *Strangers to Ourselves* offers an assessment of the human unconscious that is neither especially evil nor spiritual, but rather its role is to assist us in maneuvering through our daily lives. In Wilson's research, the unconscious mind is shown to house the bulk of our practical decision-making equipment, conveniently tucked away in the back rooms of our cognitive machinery. Wilson argues that what this form of the unconscious does for us is useful and adaptive. He demonstrates that this unconscious process manages most of our lower-level functions that occur without our being aware, and he defines the unconscious as a set of mental processes that are not accessible to consciousness but that influence our judgments, feelings, and behavior.

Wilson, William Griffith - (November 26, 1895 – January 24, 1971) - He was also known as Bill Wilson or Bill W. and was the co-founder of Alcoholics Anonymous (AA), an international mutual aid fellowship with more than two million members belonging to more than 100,000 groups of alcoholics helping other alcoholics achieve and maintain sobriety. Following AA's Twelfth Tradition of anonymity, Wilson is commonly known as "Bill W." or "Bill." After Wilson's death in 1971, his full name was included in obituaries.

In 1934, Wilson received a visit from an old drinking buddy named Ebby Thatcher. Wilson was surprised to find that Thatcher had remained sober for several weeks under the guidance of the evangelical Christian Oxford Group. Wilson took some interest in the group, but shortly after Thacher's visit, he was again admitted to Towns Hospital to recover from an episode of drinking. This was his fourth and last stay at Towns Hospital under the care of Dr. William Silkworth. It was while undergoing treatment with belladonna that Wilson experienced his spiritual conversion and stopped drinking. According to Wilson, while lying in bed depressed and despairing, he cried out, "I'll do anything! Anything at all! If there be a God, let Him show Himself!" He then had the sensation of a bright light, a feeling of ecstasy, and a new serenity. He never drank again for the remainder of his life. Wilson described his experience to Dr. Silkworth, who told him, "Something has happened to you that I don't understand. But you had better hang on to it".

Wollert, Richard - American psychologist who works primarily with sex offenders. Taught psychology at Lewis and Clark College.

Yalom, Irvin David - (born on June 13, 1931) - American psychiatrist who was an author and professor at Stanford University. His writing on existential psychology centers on what he referred to as the four "givens" of the human condition: isolation, meaninglessness, mortality and freedom. Yalom discussed ways in which individuals can respond to such concerns either in a functional or dysfunctional manner. He wrote extensively about group psychotherapy. He also published several novels, including *Lying on the Couch.*

Zehr, Howard J. - (born July 2, 1944) - American criminologist. Zehr is a pioneer of the modern concept of restorative justice. He is a Distinguished Professor of Restorative Justice at Eastern Mennonite University's Center for Justice and Peacebuilding and serves as the co-director of the Zehr Institute for Restorative Justice.

Glossary

Abilify - (aripiprazole) - Antipsychotic medication. It works by changing the actions of chemicals in the brain. It is used to treat the symptoms of psychotic conditions such as schizophrenia and bipolar disorder (manic depression). It is also used in combination with other medications to treat major depressive disorder in adults.

ADHD – (attention deficit hyperactivity disorder) - A problem of not being able to focus, being overactive, not being able control behavior, or a combination of these. For these problems to be diagnosed as ADHD, they must be out of the normal range for a person's age and development.

Alcoholics Anonymous - An international fellowship of men and women who have had a drinking problem. It is nonprofessional, self-supporting, multiracial, and apolitical. It is available almost everywhere. There is no age or educational requirement. Membership is open to anyone who wants to stop abusing alcohol.

Altruism - The principle or practice of concern for the welfare of others. It is a traditional virtue in many cultures and a core aspect of various religious traditions and secular worldviews. The concept of "others" toward whom concern should be directed can vary among cultures and religions. Altruism or selflessness is the opposite of selfishness. The term altruism was first used by the French philosopher Auguste Comte as an antonym of egoism. It was derived from the Italian word "altrui" which originally came from the Latin term "alteri", meaning "other people" or "someone else".

Altruism in biological organisms is defined as an individual performing an action that is at a cost to themselves, such as time, quality of life, pleasure, or the possibility of survival and reproduction. However, the individual could receive an intrinsic reward in the form of personal gratification, therefore the validity of this argument depends on whether an intrinsic reward qualifies as a benefit.

The term altruism can also refer to an ethical doctrine which claims that individuals are morally obligated to benefit others. In this case, it is usually contrasted with egoism, which is defined as acting to benefit one's own self.

ARNP - Advanced registered nurse practitioner.

Better mousetrap - In 1889, author and minister Ralph Waldo Emerson reportedly said "If a man can write a better book, preach a better sermon, or make a better mousetrap than his neighbor, the world will beat a path to his door".

Blank slates - According to theory of "tabula rasa", mental content comes only from experience. The meaning of tabula rasa originates from the Latin terms "blank slate" or "white paper". This means that a person is born with an empty mind that is to be filled with his or her life experiences. English philosopher John Locke, who believed in tabula rasa theory, claimed that "all ideas come from sensation or reflection". This idea was later perpetuated by the behaviorists Watson and Skinner.

Bonding - The formation of a close human relationship, as between friends. An example of bonding would be discovering the comforts of male bonding in a men's support group.

Bottom-up processing - Assigns and promotes processing from the individual person at a very basic level, in the spirit of democracy. It is the belief that intelligence most often stems from the least powerful upward rather than from the top down.

Collective wisdom - Also called group wisdom, it is shared knowledge arrived at by groups of individuals.

Content versus process in group - Content theories focus on factors within a person that energize, direct, sustain and stop behavior. These theories address the specific needs that motivate people. Content theorists include Abraham Maslow, David McClelland, Clayton Alderfer and Federick Herzberg. These theories have been helpful in explaining motivation, although some have not been verified through research. Process theories provide a description and analysis of how behavior is energized, directed, sustained, and stopped.

Correctional officer – A person who maintains security within a correctional institution and oversees the health and safety of staff and prisoners. Physically patrols and visually inspects units, yards, buildings, prisoners, prisoner property and clothing, etc., to ensure welfare, safety and security.

Dialogue - An exchange of ideas or opinions on a particular issue, especially a political or religious matter, with a goal of reaching an amicable agreement or settlement. This term can also refer to a literary work in the form of a conversation, such as a dialogue of the philosopher Plato.

Disenfranchise - To remove or block the right to vote.

DNP - Doctor of nursing practice degree.

DSM Diagnoses - Drug companies take marketing advantage of the loose DSM definitions and diagnostic criteria by promoting the misleading idea that everyday life problems are actually undiagnosed psychiatric illnesse caused by a chemical imbalance and requiring a solution in pill form. The DSM-5 was presented at the annual meeting of the American Psychiatric Association (APA), in San Francisco, in 2013. It was attended by 13,000 psychiatrists and other mental health professionals.

The DSM is written in plain language, has 947 pages and includes diagnostic criteria and insurance billing codes for a wide variety of conditions including kleptomania, gambling disorder, schizophrenia, post-traumatic stress disorder and insomnia. The release of a new medical text doesn't usually generate the kind of excitement of a new Harry Potter novel or iPhone model, but the DSM is an exception.

Other new diagnoses in the DSM include hoarding behavior and cannabis withdrawal, while eliminating and combining other diagnoses. For instance, sexual aversion disorder was redacted from the legitimate diagnoses because of "rare use and lack of supporting research", according to the APA. Until the 1970s, the DSM also classified homosexuality as a disorder.

Dyad - Two things of a similar kind or nature, or group and dyadic communication. It may also refer to the inter-relationship between the pair. In practice, this relationship refers to dialogic relations or face-to-face verbal communication between two people involving the sharing of their mutual ideas, thoughts, behaviors, ideals, likes, and dislikes, as well as questions and answers about the meaning of life.

Sociologists define a dyad as (from Greek dýo, "two" or Sanskrit "Dayadaha") as a group of two people, the smallest possible social group. As an adjective, "dyadic" describes their interaction. The pair of individuals in a dyad can be linked via romantic interest, family relation, interests, work, partners in crime, and so on. The relation can be based on equality, but may be based on an asymmetrical or hierarchical relationship (master-servant).The strength of the relationship is evaluated on the basis of time the individuals spend together, as well as on the emotional intensity of their relationship.

Dynamic process - A process that is ongoing and changing over time.

Emmanuel Movement - A psychologically-based approach to religious healing that was introduced in 1906 as an outreach of the Emmanuel Church in Boston, Massachusetts. In practice, the religious element was de-emphasized and the primary treatment modalities were individual and group therapy. Episcopal priests Samuel McComb and Elwood Worcester established a clinic at the church, which offered both medical and psychological services for twenty-three years. The primary long term influence of the Emmanuel movement, however, was on the treatment of alcoholism.

Erhard Seminars Training (EST) - An organization founded by Werner H. Erhard. It was offered as a two-weekend (60 hour) course known officially as "The EST Standard Training". The purpose was to transform one's ability to experience living, so that the situations a person had been trying to change or had been putting up with clear up just in the process of life itself. The EST training was offered from 1971 to 1984.

Evangelical posture – A position taken by an evangelical seeking to convince someone else of a particular set of religious beliefs, and is steadfast in his or her posture or attitude.

Evolutionary psychology - The goal of research in evolutionary psychology is to discover and understand the design of the human mind. Evolutionary psychology is an approach to psychology in which knowledge and principles from evolutionary biology are put to use in research on the structure of the human mind. It is not an area of study, like vision, reasoning, or social behavior. It is a way of thinking about psychology that can be applied to any topic within it, according to Leda Cosmides and John Tooby, the directors of the Center for Evolutionary Psychology at the University of California, Santa Barbara.

Functional magnetic resonance (fMRI) - A technique for measuring brain activity. It works by detecting the changes in blood oxygenation and flow.

Gestalt therapy - An existential and experiential form of psychotherapy that emphasizes personal responsibility and focuses upon the individual's experience in the present moment, the therapist-client relationship, the environmental and social contexts of a person's life, and the self-regulating adjustments people make as a result of their overall situation. Gestalt therapy was developed by Fritz Perls, Laura Perls and Paul Goodman during the 1940s and 1950s.

Head Start - A program of the United States Department of Health and Human Services that provides comprehensive early childhood education, health, nutrition, and parental involvement services to low-income children and their families.

Hundredth monkey – The knowledge of a new idea. The theory behind this phenomenon originated with Lawrence Blair and Lyall Watson in the mid-to-late 1970s. The theory was reportedly based on observations by Japanese scientists. One of the primary factors in the promulgation of the story is that some authors quote sources in which the original data and observations may have been misrepresented.

An analysis of the relevant literature by Ron Amundson, published by the Skeptics Society, revealed several key points that demystified the supposed effect. He found unsubstantiated claims that there was a sudden and remarkable increase in the proportion of monkeys washing sweet potatoes in the first observed population. Rather than all the monkeys mysteriously learning this skill, the author was noted that it was predominantly younger monkeys that learned the skill from the older monkeys through observational learning over time, which is widespread in the animal kingdom. Older monkeys who did not know how to wash tended not to learn. As the older monkeys died and younger monkeys were born the proportion of washers naturally increased. The time span between observations by the Japanese scientists was on the order of years so the increase in the proportion did not happen suddenly.

The original claim that the practice spread suddenly to other isolated populations of monkeys was called into question, given that at least one washing monkey swam to another population and spent about four years there. The monkeys also had the same researchers in common. Amundson also noted that sweet potatoes were not available to the monkeys prior to human intervention.

Instinctive - Of, relating to, or prompted by instinct, such as an instinctual ability to build a nest. It happens without thought or consciousness, and arises from impulse or natural inclination.

Indirect evidence - Much of the information researchers find does not provide an explicit answer to any defined problem; however, it can appear to be potentially relevant, especially if thoughtful researchers are watching for patterns and parallels within all available resources. Indirect evidence may support the direct evidence that has been found or that the researchers want to believe. It could also seem tangential, although no one can say exactly how. Whatever role it plays, it carries no weight until it is combined with other evidence to arrive at an answer or to construct an argument for a particular conclusion.

Intuition - A phenomenon of the mind that describes the ability to acquire knowledge without inference or the use of reason. The word "intuition" comes from Latin verb "intueri", translated as "consider", or from the middle English word intuit, "to contemplate". Intuition is often interpreted as being glimpses of greater knowledge, which is only a function of the mind; however, processes by which and why it happens typically remain mostly unknown to the thinker, as opposed to the view of rational thinking.

Little Book of Circle Processes - This book explores the peacemaking potential of a storytelling practice drawn from ancient Native American traditions. Circles can bring together people as equals for honest exchanges about the challenges each has encountered. Circles provide a time-honored peacemaking approach that is consistent with modern desires of social groups to be democratic and inclusive. Participants can learn from the wisdom of other members of the circle. Group members sit in a circle facing one another, with no table between them. There may be objects in the center that have some shared meaning to serve as a focus for the group. The dialogue is regulated by a talking piece, which can be any object that is passed around the circle. It grants the holder the sole right to speak. Circle processes can be used in a broad range of contexts, such as classrooms, workplaces, churches, etc. Circles are used for a variety of purposes such as talking, understanding, healing, support, community building, conflict resolution, and celebration.

Metaphorically speaking - A metaphor is a figure of speech to which a term or phrase is applied, or something to which it is not literally applicable in order to suggest a resemblance, as in "A mighty fortress is our God".

Morph - To be transformed. For example: morphing from a tough negotiator to Mr. Friendly.

National Training Labs (NTL) - NTL began in 1946, with the vision of Kurt Lewin, founder of modern social psychology and a pioneer in the field of action research. Lewin concluded from his research that increased awareness of self and others could be accomplished through facilitated group dialogue in Training groups (or T-groups) that advocate open- minded appreciation and inclusion of differences. He wrote that T-group participants who learned by experience, rather than reading and lecture, provided high potential for diagnostic study, evaluation and changing behaviors. His conclusions formed the basis for the NTL group learning experience.

Neuroimaging - The process of producing images of the structure or activity of the brain or other part of the nervous system by techniques such as magnetic resonance imaging or computerized tomography.

Oxford Group - A Christian organization founded by American Christian missionary Dr. Frank Buchman that believed that the root of all problems were the personal problems of fear and selfishness and that the answer was to surrender their lives over to God's Plan or God's control. Buchman was an American Lutheran minister of Swiss descent who in 1908 had a conversion experience in a chapel in Keswick, England, and as a result of that experience he would later found a movement called A First Century Christian Fellowship in 1921, which eventually became known as the Oxford Group by 1931.

Personality - The term "personality trait" refers to enduring personal characteristics that are revealed in a particular pattern of behavior in a variety of situations and are stable over time. Personality may be determined through a variety of tests, such as the Minnesota Multiphasic Personality Inventory (MMPI-2), Rorschach Inkblot test, Neurotic Personality Questionnaire KON-2006 or the Thematic Apperception Test(TAT). The most popular technique is the self-report inventory - a series of answers to a questionnaire that asks participants to indicate the extent to which sets of statements or adjectives accurately describe their own behavior or mental state.

Psychiatry - The medical specialty devoted to the study, diagnosis, treatment, and prevention of mental disorders. These include various affective, behavioral, cognitive, and perceptual abnormalities.

Psychodrama - An action method, often used as psychotherapy, in which clients use spontaneous dramatization, role playing and dramatic self-presentation to investigate and gain insight into their lives. Developed by Jacob L. Moreno, MD, psychodrama includes elements of theater, often conducted on a stage where props can be used. By closely recreating real-life situations, and acting them out in the present, participants have the opportunity to evaluate their behavior and more deeply understand a particular situation in their lives.

Psychodrama can be used in a variety of clinical and community-based settings, and is most often utilized in a group scenario, in which each person in the group can become a therapeutic agent for others' scenes. Psychodrama is not, however, a form of group therapy, and is instead an individual psychotherapy that is executed from within a group.

Religiosity - In its narrowest sense, religiosity deals more with how religious a person is, and less with how a person is religious (in practicing certain rituals, retelling certain stories, revering certain symbols, or accepting certain doctrines about deities and afterlife).

Restorative justice - An approach to justice that focuses on the needs of the victims and the offenders, as well as the involved community, instead of satisfying abstract legal principles or punishing the offender. Victims take an active role in the process, while offenders are encouraged to take responsibility for their actions, "to repair the harm they've done - by apologizing, returning stolen money, or community service".

Additionally, restorative justice provides help for offenders in order to avoid future offenses. It is based on a theory of justice that considers crime and wrongdoing to be an offence against an individual or community, rather than the government. Restorative justice that fosters dialogue between victim and offender shows the highest rates of offender accountability and victim satisfaction.

Science – "A method of discovery, nothing more and nothing less." - Stewart Springer. "Science, my boy, is made up of mistakes, but they are mistakes which it is useful to make, because they lead little by little to the truth." - Jules Verne, *Journey to the Center of the Earth.*

Secularization - The transformation of a society from close identification with religious values and institutions toward nonreligious (or irreligious) values and secular institutions. The secularization thesis refers to the belief that as societies progress, particularly through modernization and rationalization, religion loses its authority in all aspects of social life and governance. The term secularization is also used in the context of the lifting of monastic restrictions from a member of the clergy.

Self-help groups - Also known as mutual help, mutual aid, or support groups, are groups of people who provide mutual support for each other. In a self-help group, the members share a common problem, often a common disease or addiction. Their mutual goal is to help each other to deal with, and if possible to heal or to recover from, this problem. Although Michael K. Bartalos (1992) has pointed out the contradictory nature of the terms "self-help" and "support," the former U.S. surgeon general C. Everett Koop has said that self-help brings together two central but disparate themes of American culture, individualism, and cooperation ("Sharing Solutions" 1992).

The Selfish Gene - A book on sociobiology by Richard Dawkins, first published in 1976, with the purpose to examine the biology of selfishness and altruism. Dawkins used the term "selfish gene" as a way of popularizing a gene-centered view of evolution. From this point of view, the more two individuals are genetically related, the more sense (at the level of the genes) it makes for them to behave selflessly with each other. An organism is expected to evolve to maximize its inclusive fitness, an individual's own reproductive success, plus the success of its relatives (weighted by their relatedness).

Semipermeable membrane - A membrane (as a cell membrane) that allows some molecules to pass through but not others.

The Serenity Prayer - The common name for a prayer authored by the American theologian Reinhold Niebuhr (1892 – 1971). It has been adopted by Alcoholics Anonymous and other twelve-step programs. The best-known form is:
God, grant me the serenity to accept
the things I cannot change,
The courage to change the things I can,
And the wisdom to know the difference.

Social evolution - A sub-discipline of evolutionary biology that is concerned with social behaviors having fitness consequences for individuals other than the actor. Social behaviors can be categorized according to the fitness consequences they entail for the actor and recipient, according to British evolutionary biologist W. D. Hamilton:

- •Mutually beneficial – a behavior that increases the direct fitness of both the actor and the recipient
- •Selfish – a behavior that increases the direct fitness of the actor, but the recipient suffers a loss
- •Altruistic – a behavior that increases the direct fitness of the recipient, but the actor suffers a loss
- •Spiteful – a behavior that decreases the direct fitness of both the actor and the recipient.

    Social evolution is also often regarded (especially, in the field of social anthropology) as evolution of social systems and structures.

T-group or training group - (sometimes also referred to as sensitivity-training group, human relations training group or encounter group) – A form of group training where participants (typically, between eight and fifteen people) learn about themselves and about small group processes in general, through their interactions with one another. They use feedback, problem solving, and role play to gain insights into themselves, others, and groups of people.

About the Authors

Dr. Philip Springer is a retired psychiatrist and a former general practitioner in rural Mississippi. He developed the Double Circle Group while on the faculty at the University of Florida. Throughout his career, he has concentrated on peer-directed group process using his experience in Alcoholics Anonymous as well as his early training at the National Training Labs in Bethel, Maine. He resides in Gainesville, Florida.

Dr. Shelby Havens is a psychiatric and primary care nurse practitioner. She worked for many years with chronically mentally ill patients in Florida prisons and jails. She currently teaches in a bachelors degree program in Health Care Administration at City College and sees patients at the Helping Hands Clinic, a facility that provides health care services for homeless clients. Shelby lives in Gainesville, Florida.